WITH A P. ___ ᴊᴀʟᴛ

*Food for Thought from
Tyne and Esk Writers*

edited by Margaret Skea

British Library Cataloguing in Publication Data:
a catalogue record for this publication
is available from the British Library

ISBN   978-1-912052-83-7

© Tyne and Esk Writers 2023

Typeset in 12pt Minion Pro at Haddington, Scotland

Cover and printing by by West Port Print and Design, St Andrews

Contents

Foreword

I have had the privilege of serving as Creative Writing Fellow for Tyne and Esk Writers – a collective of writing groups spread across the Lothians – for just over two years, separated by the pandemic. Although linked under the Tyne and Esk banner, each group is unique with a diverse range of members; a diversity which is reflected in this anthology. Each member was invited to submit a small selection of their work - fiction, non-fiction, poetry or prose and guaranteed at least one piece included. All submissions were also entered into the Tyne and Esk annual 'Writer of the Year' competition.

In recognition of a grant from Tesco, the chosen theme for this collection is 'Food' – in the broadest sense of the word – and the interpretations of the theme are indeed broad.

Food is universal, essential in physical terms, but often also related to emotional need and frequently used as a displacement activity. Often the 'surface' story of a submission overlays a much deeper, thought-provoking message or theme – both the prose and poetry winning entries for the Writer of the Year competition are multi-layered. Within the general theme, specific topics vary widely, from social commentary to war; from the environment and industrialisation to family dynamics; from love, loss and emotional guilt to laugh out loud humour; from dementia and isolation to sci-fi and stories with a 'twist-in-the-tale'. It is fascinating to see very different treatments of the same subject by different authors. How we approach and react to food varies widely from culture to culture and that too is evidenced here.

The quality of the entries made the task of judging the competition and choosing pieces for inclusion in the anthology difficult. In addition, though the submissions were anonymised, I was concerned that having worked closely with the groups, I might be hampered by guessing the authors of individual pieces. I couldn't have been more wrong, for when, post-selection, the authors' names were revealed, in most cases I was taken by surprise. That is a tribute to the range of skills of each of the writers represented. I am delighted to have been involved in this project, for the collection is a worthy addition to any bookshelf. Readers will be entertained, moved and have their thinking challenged, which is, after all, what creative writing should be all about.

Margaret Skea
October 2023

Editor's Note:

Four prose items have been formatted with a line between paragraphs to indicate that they are non-fiction items.

The Perfect Holiday Supper . . .

What could be better? A return to our favourite Italian destination, a table in the courtyard, a balmy evening. It was ten years since we'd first brought our daughters Diane and Denise here, a decade in which we'd all changed but the charm and warmth of the hilltop village hadn't altered.

Our food arrived and my wife, Dorothy, tucked into her mushroom risotto exclaiming over every delicious mouthful. Denise had to be reminded to put her phone down before her dinner got cold – it seemed more important to get the perfect selfie: the pout just right, the evening sun adding a glow to her bare shoulders, dark eyes framed by improbable lashes, and the best possible alignment of her multi-layered burger with the lurid Aperol Spritz in the background. I was delighted by my simple pasta and ragout; I chose it on every visit.

And Diane, well to be honest, I could hardly bear to even look at her. In the periphery of my vision, I could tell that she was picking over her meagre salad. Moving greenery around her plate, not much of it making the journey to her mouth. Despite the mild climate she was shrouded in a black anorak, the hood was up. In direct contrast to Denise's uptilted face, Diane was round-shouldered, eyes cast towards her plate, hair hanging limply around her face.

I know it's unkind, but I can't help thinking that she might feel better if her hair was washed and shiny – maybe even styled in some way. She'd certainly look better. And maybe keeping the greasy strands from her face might improve the acne, which seems to have been a permanent feature of the past year. Sunlight on her cheeks, a slight tan across her nose – wouldn't any of that brighten her mood, and appearance?

Denise wriggles around in her strappy top flirting with unknown boys at the adjacent table. She's aware that they're looking at her appreciatively and it only increases her self-confidence. A knowing glance passes between me and her mother and Dorothy gives an admonishing cough and the kind or warning look that only a mother can . . . The preening stops and Denise turns kindly to her older sister, hand gently on her sleeve: 'How's the food, Di?'

Diane nods almost imperceptibly. 'It's fine', and having tolerated Denise's touch for long enough she moves from reach and stirs the salad some more. The sleeves of her jacket are pulled down, covering her hands. There is almost nothing of my daughter on show.

I know all of this without having to watch. It's a scene played out so often, and I hate every moment of it. I hate my wife's irrepressible optimism. I hate the ease with which Denise sails through life. I hate the guilt that overwhelms me.

It started nearly four years ago – before there was any thought of virus or restriction, a time when young people partied as they should, when they were educated with their peers, when holidays were commonplace and life seemed untroubled.

I was at home alone, Dorothy at choir practice, Di at a party and Denise spending the evening at her pal's house. The phone rang. Yes, we still maintain the quaint, fixed-line house phone. I'd just taken the cap off a bottle and I poured my beer with one hand while picking up the receiver with the other. 'Dad, it's really boring here, can you come and pick me up?'

'I thought Alice's Mum was getting you later. Is Alice not there?'

'Yeah, it's just not really my scene here, you know, not my crowd.'

I *know* I had sighed at that moment. Diane would have heard it, and felt it.

'Please Dad' she wheedled.

I looked at my beer, golden, foamy, delicious, I noticed the condensation forming on the glass, and at the two empty bottles on the table beside it. It was less than 3 miles to the house where I'd dropped Di off earlier, I hadn't had *that* much to drink, the roads would be quiet

... but the cool enticement of the promised liquor swayed my decision. 'Sorry love. I've had a few beers, it's not safe. You'll just have to wait it out until Alice is ready to leave. See you later. Don't be out too long.'

I returned the phone to its cradle, switched on the golf channel, settled back on the sofa and took a long drink from my glass. I possibly dozed off but jerked awake at the sound of the front door closing. It was still light outside.

'Diane?'

There was no answer. Then quiet footfall going upstairs. A bag dropped on a bedroom floor (the small room at the front) then the firm close and lock of the bathroom door. I followed up and knocked hesitantly: 'All OK? Did Alice's Mum come early?'

There was a gap during which I could hear only the running of bath water. 'It's fine.' 'I'm just tired.'

I thought, or imagined, that I'd heard a sob. But the splashing of water drowned out any further sound, and respect for my daughter's privacy saw me hesitate and retreat.

I didn't think to mention anything to Dorothy when she returned full of excitement about an upcoming concert. By that time, both girls were in their rooms – tucked up in bed listening to music on their headphones – or whatever teenagers did in their own secret space. Denise had hugged me goodnight as she passed from bathroom to bedroom after cleaning her teeth. Diane mumbled something that might have been 'night' or 'help' or something else altogether too awful to contemplate.

She was never the same again.

The following morning, a Saturday, had not been unusual. Neither Di nor Denise were up by 10 am when I left to play golf. Dorothy was going shopping. The girls could get their own breakfast. What was unusual was Alice's appearance at the door late afternoon.

'Di's not answering my calls. Is she OK?'

'Eh yeah.'

'Just, she left the party early, and I thought she might be mad with me . . .'

'You didn't come home together?'

'Err . . . well, no. I was, well . . . with someone . . .'

Against my rising force of annoyance that Diane had been so stupid, Dot was the voice of calm and reason.

'I'll go and tell her you're here, Alice.'

Apparently, Diane had a migraine (was that a euphemism for period pain?) and wanted to stay in the dark. Dorothy said she'd get Di to call Alice later, maybe tomorrow.

'What on earth were those girls thinking?' I raged once the front door had closed. 'She's home and safe, but how often do we tell them to stick together, to watch out for each other?'

None of us know what happened in the hour and a half between Diane leaving the party to walk home on her own, and her quiet arrival at our house. She hasn't even said that anything DID happen, at least not to me, or to Dorothy. All we know is what we can see. A vibrant personality suddenly shut down. A retreat into herself, into the shadows of her room with the curtains constantly closed. Refusal to see friends or go to school. Inability to engage in family life. Silent tears at every mealtime as yet another plate is pushed away, the food barely touched.

We know the frustration of a health system which fails to offer enough care or support for young people, we count the cost of trips to see counsellors on a private basis. We are all too familiar with the agonising wait for news following another unsuccessful attempt at suicide. We see our daughter's shame as she hides her scarred arms and legs and body. We hear her vomiting after being forced to eat something nourishing and filling. Despite being engulfed in over-sized apparel we can detect her scrawny skeletal frame.

I don't know what we hoped to get from this holiday – a miraculous cure? The disclosure of some awful event which might start a journey towards healing? Selfishly I hope for reassurance that nothing untoward had happened and this was merely a sad coincidence of a sudden onset of mental crisis, rather than the dreadful nagging feeling that I might have let my daughter down.

As we sit in the soft light of an Italian evening, Dorothy hopes her normality and enthusiasm will make everything all right again. Denise vacillates between tender concern for her sister and blythe unconcern for all the challenges of life.

I look at Di, properly, for the first time this evening. I read hurt, bewilderment, lostness. I see revulsion as she puts a morsel of tomato onto her fork and slowly raises it towards her mouth. I look at the cold beer on the table in front of me, golden, foamy, delicious, condensation forming on the glass, and at the two empty bottles on the table beside it. And I feel sick with guilt.

Jane Patmore (*2023 Prose winner of Writer of the Year*)

Hierarchy

When you are at the back end of society, you look for others to look down on. I may have been poor and living in a deprived slum, but at least I was not pond life like the large poor families. The Howies were a street fighting family team. The brothers kept disappearing off to borstal and later prison. For all their housebreaking and stealing, they were always poor. Joe Howie used to follow my group of friends looking for a date with either one of us. His teeth had a constant green layer of something over them and his clothes were torn. His mother used to steal stuff off the rag and bone man's cart to clothe her large brood. At the time I was a member of the Smith family, and we were superior to them as we bought our clothes from catalogues and paid for them in weekly instalments. No member of the Smith family had been in prison, making us a cut above the Howies.

The Dirty Doak's poverty was like a dull grey aura that made others shy away from them. I was at school with one of the sons, he was faecally incontinent and had a desk set away from the other pupils. He was badly bullied and had a terrible time of it. There was around a dozen Doaks. Ella, the matriarch, seemed to be constantly pregnant. Day upon day she wore the same grey stripy dress under a huge navy blue Astrakhan coat. Even in winter she never wore tights, and only wore cheap black plimsoles on her feet. We were told not to stare at her pendulum breasts that swung from side to side as she walked. The Smiths were Church of Scotland and attended a Victorian red sandstone church exclusively for weddings, funerals, and baptisms. The Doaks were devout members of the Apostolic Church, that they attended in an almost daily basis. Their church was no more than a corrugated iron ramshackle construction with 'Jesus Saves' scrawled in bad handwriting above the door. The Smiths were obviously better than them!

The Clatty Clarks lived on a diet of chips made in a nasty cauldron of a pan that caught fire so often that Social Work installed an industrial sized extinguisher in their home. The family were so overweight that some of them could not walk. I knew their daughter, Big Aggie. She took me into her house once. There was no chairs or other furnishings you would normally see in a home, just double beds taking up the three rooms. One room had three two beds where the younger children slept. Another room had three double beds for the teenagers, with the last small room having one double bed for the parents. The Smiths were better than the Clarks, we ate other fried food besides chips and had furniture.

The Dirty Doaks, Clatty Clarks and Howies all thought they were better than the Smiths. They had inside toilets and baths whereas the Smiths had an outside toilet that they shared with two other families, and had no hot running water in the house. Moira, the matriarch of the Smith household, was a single parent. The Doaks, Clarks and Howies were poor, but at least they had both parents at home. The Smith family was made up of foundlings. Moira had her own son, but also long term fostered me and a Pakistani boy who she insisted was Italian and renamed David. The only reason we ate well was because Moira was having an affair with the local butcher, so we also had sausages to fry with the chips in our manky frying pan.

Alison Low (highly commended)

Names have been changed to preserve anonymity.

Food for Furlough

He was furloughed for the best part of a year. I worked on, NHS, at full pelt. He took over the role of chief domestic engineer and I reluctantly stepped down as the strain of 13 hour shifts on the Covid ward took their toll.

At first I thought his shopping was strange. His meals over-complicated. Perhaps I'd have done it better. Slowly I realised what was happening.

He was a-moving and a-shaking our kitchen. Borlotti beans, pak Choi, huge bunches of fresh herbs and panko breadcrumbs were appearing. And aubergines. Plump and blackly gleaming and suddenly, unexpectedly delicious. I drove home exhausted, hungry, depleted of all my strengths and wow . . . the aroma of Italy was wafting upstairs, tantalising me as I showered all traces of the day away. Aubergines parmigiana. Slippery and savoury with a crumb crunch, a deep continental tomato-ness I'd only ever tasted in restaurants until now, strings of mozzarella landing on my chin as I refuelled. His food restored body and soul. Fresh tomatoes by the dozen entered our fridge and were metamorphosed into sauce which wove savoury magic round each ingredient it touched.

He chopped to the sounds of jazz, Northern soul and John Martyn which belted out of the kitchen accompanied by the joyous smells of dinner. His Christmas stocking knife pounded on the wooden board – mounds of fresh stuff to process. Home made tagliatelle dangled from the pulley like old tights – as light as a feather and a delight to swallow.

A simple potato in many forms. Boiled, crushed, buttery and herby, baked with a crispy salty skin, sautéed into crunchy deliciousness, all ingredients were safe in his patient hands.

Dhal many ways. Yellow with garlic or dark brown and deep with smoked paprika. Sustaining and solid and great for my packed lunch the next day.

Focaccia bread wrapped in a clean tea towel with crystals of salt and sprigs of rosemary from the garden nestling in its dimples.

Timing and seasoning. Hard to perfect, but that year gave him room for mastery. I watched in awe as a cabinet reshuffle took place, fridge and cupboards were rearranged and it all made sense. He was happy, spinning salads, whizzing nuts, reducing sauces and most of all, watching us descend hungrily and clean our plates.

That year was a gift for us all. Facing the new order of things, united by meals in our family kitchen. We were lucky.

Ali MacDougall (commended)

Etiquette

There I was, sitting next to Her Majesty at a Charity Banquet. In all my finery – well, in Moss Bros's finery – I more or less matched the other men at the tables, but that didn't altogether put me at my ease. Many of them wore an array of medals, whereas I lacked such ornamental accessories.

I had bought the raffle ticket without really looking at the potential prizes. I assumed there might be a Christmas hamper or a bottle of port. When the invitation dropped on the mat, I was utterly amazed. 'Her Majesty Queen Elizabeth II has pleasure . . .' My first reaction was to send an apology. But everyone said: 'Don't do that. Sleep on it; you might feel differently in the morning.' Well, I didn't sleep much, but in the morning I thought: why not? It'll be an experience.

It hadn't occurred to me that the Royal Family would ever get involved in this sort of thing. I knew that in the past some aristos had been persuaded to have the hoi polloi for dinner – as guests I mean. The Duke of Bedford years ago, for instance, had adopted a very commercial attitude to making money for the upkeep of his estate. But, the Queen . . . ?

Anyway, I concocted what I hoped was a suitable reply and sent it off to Buckingham Palace. The response confirmed my participation. The prize included a stay at the Dorchester, and a chauffeur-driven limousine was to be at my disposal. I turned up at the Palace and joined the stream of cars. I had, of course, been prepared for the necessary protocol. Once inside, I was greeted by the Queen, and joined her in the procession to the enormous, richly decorated ballroom. Tables formed a U shape and we were led to the high table which allowed a view down both the longer lines which filled the space. Beefeaters, who were unlikely to eat anything, lined the walls, and various servants, 'flunkeys' I suppose, moved around making sure everything was in order.

The Queen made a short speech in which she introduced her 'guest', the raffle winner (although she didn't actually call me that) and she sat down. Now she turned to me with a smile. 'I don't often have the opportunity to talk with people who are not politicians or diplomats or aristocrats, Mr Williams. I am so pleased to have your company this evening.'

'I don't often get to talk to a queen, Ma'am. You are very kind. I do hope my table manners will be up to the occasion.'

'I am sure you will manage perfectly.'

'You haven't seen how I normally eat peas Ma'am!'

The Queen turned to me and – I'm pretty sure of this – she winked. 'When we are together in the family we all scoop them in the hollow of our forks like everyone else. But at banquets I never allow peas to be served. And peas are not the only things. The chefs' instructions are very detailed. There is a specification listing dishes and ingredients which are not approved. Nothing which cannot be gathered on the prongs of a fork is permitted.'

'So, no snails then; or oysters or crabs from the shell.'

'That's right.'

'I guess banquets never include spaghetti?'

'Oh dear no.'

'I note that you drink your soup very "properly". I have to admit that I take anything, including soup, which needs a spoon by drawing the spoon towards me; except right now, of course. And I don't tip the soup bowl away from me.'

'Yes. That is a bit of a formality.'

'I believe the origin of that piece of etiquette is the perceived danger of tipping the contents into your lap. You would have to be very careless for that to happen.'

'Indeed. But I do follow the "rules" where that is concerned.'

'How do you deal with gravy or sauce? I like to have bread with a dish of that kind, so that I can dip pieces in – *à la française* – to absorb what it would be a pity to miss.'

'Ah. We have some almost square plates – I believe they come from Ikea – which allow you to gather the gravy to the corner and then tip it into your mouth. You won't whisper a word of this to anyone will you?'

'Of course not, Ma'am, but I am enjoying our talk – as much as the meal.'

'So am I Mr Williams. It makes such a change from the usual chitchat.'

The banquet proceeded, as did our conversation. The food was very good, but I took particular note of how it all conformed to the principles that the Queen had described. I won't make you envious by giving you a course-by-course description. But there was poultry. 'From the way you have spoken, I guess that when dining normally you emulate Charles Laughton as your forebear Henry VIII and throw the gnawed chicken bones back over your shoulder.'

The Queen smiled. 'Actually, no. The carpets are very expensive and it would be a pity to spoil them. And I am not too keen on gnawing bones.'

We went on to discuss a few likes and dislikes. The Queen's tastes tended towards British cooking – and accepted the etiquette. I didn't ask her if she had ever had fish and chips from a newspaper!

The courses continued until a bell introduced short speeches related to the charity. Finally, before it was obviously the end of the meal, I put a suggestion to my hostess.

'You know, Your Majesty, I could give you a raffle ticket so that you can come and have a meal at our house. I'm sure you would enjoy it. We have Ikea plates too.'

Graham Leake *(commended)*

Eating my Feelings

Restricting my intake, so not to be polluted,
Purging all the excess, ashamed of my needs.
Demonising food I rely on for survival,
Afraid of being seen, yet fearing the reprisal.

Counting all the calories and doing all the maths,
Aiming for perfection so I'll never feel the crash
Of all my shame and disconnection, hiding all my fears
Abstaining and withdrawing so no one sees my tears.

Avoiding all the pain inside by making it go numb
Sacrificing what I need to protect my bloody Mum
And others who say they are more important than my needs,
I cannot live on bread alone but I can if it's got cheese.

Analysing every word in case I get it wrong,
Judging my own reactions to the other person's song
About the girl, the one that got away, she's probably in hiding,
Like me, can't face the day and thinks of suiciding.

Drowning all my sorrows, Drambuie is my friend
Who takes me on a journey to the very bitter end
Of myself and all that I am feeling, at last my head is quiet.
I'm hoping that I'll sleep tonight, my body's very tired.

I binge on everything I can, trying to numb my pain,
Consuming people by the dozen, trying to stay sane
I cling and I obsess, attaching way too fast
Hoping for some light relief from the pain of coming last.

Last in terms of priority, I place myself too low,
I cannot set a boundary and I'm scared of saying no.
If only I could know my worth and rectify my blindness
I'd find myself free at last with much more loving-kindness.

Katrina Hadland (*2023 Poetry winner of Writer of the Year*)

Urchin Sushi

Purple
sea urchins eat
through forests of bull kelp
from California to Norway
forming

urchin
barrens, wastelands
of desolate sea floor
leaving abalone to die of
hunger

what if
purple urchins,
caught and fed with seaweed,
sustainably produced of course,
were used,

eaten
as urchin roe,
without spines, to be sure,
served as rich, savoury sushi
on toast

kelp grows
fast, three months would
replenish the forest
ingesting carbon dioxide
for us

Diana Stevens *(highly commended)*

Buckthorn and Blackthorn

Tyninghame, a bay aflame with buckthorn
bushes, sun drop laden ragamuffins,
starry orange constellations, spotlights
on the afternoon. Perfect crop for jams

or juices, making pies, hand creams even.
We are in our forties with a daughter
of our own but, here, skin taut with sunshine,
ears full of whisper-water, I could still

be seven, eight, back at Good God Corner.
Resting up, drinking in the matchless sweep
of Harlech beach, mountainsides of Eryri,
low waves humming landward like an artist's

jagged pencil lines. I could have, just this
instant, tagged my way back up the zigzag
path. A still inflated ride-on orca stashed
across my sunblush back, plucking sloes

from blackthorn bushes, wincing at their acid kiss,
a single, molten buckthorn berry glowing in the sky.

Tammy Swift-Adams (commended)

Off

Food has gone off
    the shelves of common supermarkets, to
    beat down the mood, flag up
    that cheap and green and quick don't rhyme.

Food has gone off
    into banks and conscience laundering
    as if those stains which shame
    our time's short commons will come clean.

Food has gone off
    while half the world in dismal disarray
    waits for the Ukrainian War
    to stop, and lacks the means to pay.

Food has gone off
    the ribs of all the lovely TV stars
    who take the latest slimming
    drug, the magic pop-in pen.

Food has gone off.
    It misses old and tried preservatives,
    the salt of common sense,
    the common meal, the common weal.

Jock Stein (commended)

Parenthood and Plum Pudding

Can recollections of times past be tempered by fond memories of motherhood and apple pie or even plum pudding? Maybe they can.

I well remember my Auntie Ethel because she was the one with a glass eye. She was my grandfather's wife but we were not allowed to call her grandma out of respect for our proper grandmother, his first wife, who had died long before. They had come to visit us for a day between Christmas and New Year, one of those days when, as a seven-year-old boy, I had hoped to play with my Christmas toys unimpeded by visiting relatives or the need to write thank-you letters.

Grandfather was a Baptist minister of the Calvinist persuasion and my sisters and I had heard him preach on many a Sunday. We had witnessed his pronouncements on the fate of those who erred from the straight and narrow. Sometimes in the evening service he would work himself into a fiery rage, bang the pulpit and with a strange quivering voice describe the pangs of eternal suffering awaiting born sinners. It elicited no real fear in us children any more than the giant in a fairy tale; we thought it was just something preachers like to do. We knew he didn't really mean it because he always calmed down afterwards and gave us Fry's chocolate bars on the way out of the chapel. This was true manna from heaven and a welcome supplement to our usual Sunday evening snack of beef dripping on toast.

Our real grandmother had tried to keep body and soul together by teaching piano lessons but eventually they had to sell the piano in order to live and, like so many in the Depression between the Wars, she became utterly despondent. Our grandfather had no answer to this other than to blame his circumstances. He became obsessively fundamental and is reported to have taken refuge in his study as a hermit, demanding that his meals be supplied to the door. For her the pressure imposed by upholding the role of pastor's wife among those chapel folk was even greater. One fateful Sunday morning she feigned illness to stay at home as he went off to preach. On returning a few hours later he found a house full of gas and himself a widower.

Auntie Ethel was a lady in his chapel congregation who harboured a special adoration for her pastor and had started accompanying him everywhere. Some suggested she had been his lady-in-waiting for some time but that was unfair as she attended him purely out of a sense of duty to the pastor of her chapel. She dealt with chapel administration and consoled him in his despair but inevitably the time came when this did develop into a romance and within a timespan that was deemed too short by the family, they were married. She was never really accepted by my father, although my mother was prepared to support her and even defend her on occasions.

Back at our house, grandad and Auntie Ethel had arrived mid-morning and by half past twelve or so we were all sitting expectantly around an oval table. In modern parlance it was lunch but then the main meal of the day was always called 'dinner'. It was a time when we had school dinners served by dinner ladies.

'Be nice to your Auntie Ethel,' mum had instructed us children. Dad, I noted, had not reinforced this instruction.

The meal started with the main course and often ended with the main course. Starters were unknown except as those folk who fired a gun on school sports day. Being just after Christmas it was cold turkey, hot fried bubble and squeak, turnips and pickles. As a special, mum had produced a jar of home-made red currant jelly to go with the turkey (cranberry did not arrive until years later). Sitting next to Auntie Ethel, on her glass-eye side, I passed her the jelly first. The jar had tightly stretched cellophane over the top and I was intrigued as she repeatedly tried to poke her knife into it but felt some resistance and tried again.

The experiment was brought to a premature end: 'Just help your Auntie by taking off the top, remember she is a guest here,' admonished my mother while my young sisters suppressed their giggles.

Next came oxo gravy with instructions to pour it over the bubble and squeak. It resided in a strange gravy boat with its oval saucer bonded permanently to the base. Mum was looking at me as if I was meant to be doing something so I handed it very carefully to Auntie Ethel first . . . her being a guest. Maybe she meant me to serve her, I never knew because by then Auntie Ethel was starting to pour it. The boat was very full and the flow from the pouring edge hit the side of the bonded saucer and went everywhere. Being on the glass-eye side she failed to notice and kept pouring until stopped abruptly by my father on the other side of her. Further giggles from my sisters were accompanied by a killing look from my mother; in retrospect I suppose I was just another horrid little boy. After that, things settled down as we enjoyed the tasty meal and the plates were cleared away in anticipation of the second course. Mum announced she had made a plum pudding, a favourite among us children.

This was no ordinary plum pudding. It was made in a large white porcelain basin lined with a muslin cloth which, after filling, could be tied up over the top 'to keep the flavour in'. It consisted of a stodgy suet pudding mixture round the edge and plenty of large Victoria plums, from her stock of Kilner jars, in the middle. It was steamed for a couple of hours in the oven, not on top, until the plum juice infused into the inner white edge of the suet. The muslin could then be undone and the pudding tipped over onto a large dish and sprinkled with icing sugar. It could then be ceremoniously carried through to the waiting dinners.

Alas it was not to be. Mum appeared back, somewhat crestfallen to inform us that the gas pressure had fallen as too many households were using it and the flames were so low it had not cooked through. It would take another twenty minutes or so. She then commenced a long account of the failings of gas ovens until brought to a sudden halt by myself drawing her attention to Auntie Ethel next to me who was quietly sobbing. Even then I realised that all this talk about gas ovens and their failings was probably not the best topic for the occasion. Unfortunately, crying made her glass eye very difficult to retain in position and Auntie Ethel was by then holding a serviette around her eyes and sobbing uncontrollably. Mum kindly led her away from the dining room and escorted her upstairs where they both remained for some time.

The ensuing silence round the table was eventually broken by grandad who explained how grandma (he always called her this in spite of us not referring to her as such) was easily upset because her glass eye had once come out and rolled under the table. He told us it ran in her family and started to recount stories about relations of hers who also had eye defects. I remember even at that young age feeling uncomfortable about all this disclosure. My father abruptly reminded us that there was still a plum pudding in the oven which surely must be ready by now.

It was duly rescued, inverted onto a large plate and placed on the table. Nobody could find the icing sugar but it did not matter because it was served to each of us with custard sauce. We lapsed into silent eating until interrupted by my youngest sister who was only four years old:

'I've found a glass eye in my pudding.'

She well knew it was a plum stone and so did we, but she had a vivid imagination and it initiated an infectious fit of giggles which ended up with us all seeing who had the most 'glass eyes'. Dad said nothing and we anticipated a stern rebuke but he suddenly announced:

'I've beaten you all as I have four.'

'You had a larger portion,' I pointed out.

Further analysis of our scores was curtailed as mum and Auntie Ethel, who seemed to have recovered a little, appeared from upstairs. Mum expressed disappointment that we had proceeded without them. In the circumstances even us children thought it best to discontinue our search.

Auntie Ethel looked longingly at the table.

Dad, smiling to himself, said to her, 'I do believe you're eyeing up the pudding.'

Us children lapsed into fits of giggles and even grandad, who had remained somewhat aloof throughout, allowed a grin to spread across his face. I only managed to compose myself with difficulty as mum served Auntie Ethel a generous portion and covered it with warm custard. As Auntie Ethel sought solace in spoonfuls of plum pudding, mum gave dad a questioning look. He must have felt uneasy because he quickly issued us with the seasonal dismissal, 'Why don't you children go and play with your Christmas toys?'

Keith Cornwell

Sandwiches

Jam sandwiches. Almost synonymous with Britishness. Not the American PB and J. No, simply jam sandwiches. For me, the construction was always the same. Sliced, wholemeal bread— a well-known brand you can find in any supermarket— and the thinnest sliver of margarine. The jam of course was always strawberry, as liberal as you like with that. The brand was of little importance. If it was strawberry and it was jam, I would eat it.

As a child, that was about all I would eat. That and the odd helping of fruit. My mum despaired. She would sometimes sit down on the floor in defeat as I would pointedly refuse to eat whatever was placed in front of me. Bananas? No. Potatoes, absolutely not. They were the worst. A little chicken? Perhaps, on a good day.

To tempt me into eating my sandwiches at the very least, she would cut them into shapes using a cookie cutter. 'To my goldilocks, here are three bears for your dinner' she would wrap them in a napkin with a note to eat on my school break.

Mostly, I would eat them, but occasionally the thought of cloying bread and oily margarine would turn my stomach. On those days I would take the sandwiches, and knead them into as small a ball as possible, like play dough. Then I would sneak my lunchbox into the girl's toilets, lock myself into a cubicle and stuff the small sandwich balls behind the u-bend. I was an anxious child and this act did me no favours, my heart would pound furiously at the thought of being caught. The guilt too was almost too much to bear. The thought of my mum, thoughtfully writing out the note caused me great shame, so I pushed it to the back of my mind. At least the empty lunchbox would please her.

My brother was even worse than me. The entirely nutritionless 'sugar butty' was his favourite meal. Whilst I would only ever eat brown bread, he would only ever eat white. Definitely, unequivocally, no crusts. He had boundless energy and would slink away from the dining hall after just a few mouthfuls of sandwich to go outside for the rest of playtime. Unlike me, my brother would leave whatever he hadn't eaten of his dinner for our mum to find in his lunchbox after school. She would often say nothing and sigh, simply throwing it in the bin. Other times, she would angrily ask why he hadn't eaten his dinner. Unlike me, my brother wasn't and still isn't a people pleaser. He would always answer honestly that he hadn't wanted it.

My sister died before my brother was born. In some cruel twist of fate, out of the three of us, she was the least trouble. She would eat whatever she was given, never grumbled and was always cheerful to be fed. It must have been even more difficult then, for my mum to be left with these two whinging, sandwich eaters.

One jam on brown, one sugar on white.

By the time I was twelve, I had been shamed by my peers into eating a wider variety of dishes. Sat at some strange kitchen table I had been too embarrassed to mention to someone else's mum that I didn't eat pizza, potatoes or curry. So I tried them. Cutting them up into tiny pieces, I would try and disguise the potato with the other foods on my plate. But not the curry. Like most British people in the early 90's, I discovered the chicken tikka masala. And it was great.

For my thirteenth birthday, I asked my parents to take me for an Indian. Products of their own upbringing and only in their late thirties, my parents had never eaten a curry before. With some trepidation, my dad sampled the Chicken Korma I had insisted he order because I was convinced that he would like it. And he did. My mum, suddenly liberated from meat and two veg, became culinarily adventurous. There was no curry she wouldn't try. No level of heat was too much for her. The mighty curry became king in our household.

For years after most occasions were celebrated with a trip to Indian Heaven. It's where I had my first 'grown-up' date with my first 'proper' boyfriend. It's where my wild aunty would take me as a birthday treat. The restaurant manager, Latif knew us by name. Young and dashingly handsome, my aunt would flirt with him. And ever the professional, Latif would be just as charming in return, though always careful never to overstep the business owner/ customer boundaries. He clearly had a good radar for a wrong'un and my aunt was certainly that. We celebrated most birthdays at the restaurant, including my seventeenth. One of the eldest in my year at school, it would be my last full year at home.

My parents drove me to the University campus. They helped me unpack, dad plugged the black and white television in at the wall and fiddled with the aerial until we got a clear picture. Mum claimed me a cupboard in the kitchen where she placed a few of my favourite provisions. Me, excited and them, tearful, hugged goodbye as they left me in the safe hands of my neighbour, an older, worldly, international student who promised them she would take good care of me. Which she did. I would see them in a few weeks anyway when I would catch the train back home.

Later, lying awake in the small single bed of my tiny room, homesickness found its way in, tapping at the windows and reminding me that tomorrow was curry night and my family may well be ordering a takeaway without me.

In those quiet moments, I would sneak down to the shared kitchen with its stark walls and unfamiliar utensils and make myself a sandwich. It was always the same. Wholemeal bread, a well-known brand, the thinnest sliver of margarine and a thick helping of strawberry jam.

Emma Lamont

Subterfuge

For the rest of her life Alice was to associate *Massachusetts* by the Bee Gees with the Diet of Autumn 1967.

'Do you realise you're overweight?' The bald headed doctor set aside his stethoscope. 'That won't help your asthma. What age are you, twenty two, twenty three?'

'I - - I'm eighteen. I've been trying to reduce for my cousin's wedding next February. I'm to be chief bridesmaid.' Alice reddened.

'See the nurse! She'll sort you out with a diet sheet and keep an eye on you.'

The nurse flourished a typed sheet of A4. 'You stick to what it tells you here and I'll weigh you again in a fortnight.'

Alice scurried from the surgery. Lean meat, vegetables and fish were permitted in any quantity so long as not fried, while bread, milk and 'in-between' foods were allowed in stipulated amounts. Sweets, chocolate, ice cream, together with all of the indulgences that brought joy to her life were forbidden.

'I'll see to it that nothing you're not allowed gets anywhere near your plate.' Nancy, Alice's step mum eyed the page with approval. 'Don't even think about cheating when you're at work.'

Her workmates at the life assurance company encouraged her. 'Remember, it's for your health, you're doing it.' Mrs Jackson, the supervisor patted her arm.

* * *

She gave up going to the staff canteen with the others, settling for a few slices of lean cooked meat from British Home Stores. In keeping with the rules of the eating plan, Nancy served Alice evening meals of nutritious but bland fare. Aromas of roasts with gravy tantalised her taste buds but she held her resolve, making the best of a piece of fresh fruit while the others tucked into dessert.

Nancy observed, 'Your face isn't so chubby looking. Your diet's making a difference already. See you keep at it!' At the end of the first fortnight the nurse announced with a smile, 'Half a stone off already, Alice. Well done!'

Alice strived to stick to the new regime. By day she was busy at work and in the evenings she kept her mind off food by reading. Neighbours began to stop her in the street. 'Have you *lost weight*?' Sometimes Alice felt their tone would have been better suited to asking, had she given up robbery with violence.

When her clothes became loose the girls at work took her shopping. It was a joy to venture into boutiques and choose garments designed for her age and stage in life instead of making the best of ranges aimed at more mature women. She looked forward to the office Christmas party. This year she wouldn't spend half the evening hiding in the toilet. Now when she played *Massachusetts* on her Dansette Viva she allowed herself to fantasise about the wedding, imagining herself floating on the dance floor in the arms of the best man.

* * *

It was in the third month of the diet that the dreams started. She would wake in a sweat having dreamt she had guzzled her way through a whole packet of custard creams. Or she'd dream Nancy and the girls from work were staring aghast through the shop window having caught her in the act of queueing for fish and chips.

Then food began to dominate her daydreams. In BHS she'd find herself lingering by the sweet counter. On the way back to the office she'd take a detour by Crawford's, The Bakers, savouring smells of hot pastries and bacon rolls. In the evenings she found herself struggling to concentrate on her book. Need the occasional deviation from the diet do any harm? Just to taste one square of Cadbury's Dairy Milk would be a relief.

Things came to a head when she had a week's holiday from work. She went into town to do Christmas shopping and helped Nancy with chores round the house. No matter what activity she tried to absorb herself in, forbidden food invaded her thoughts. When Nancy went out one morning Alice could contain herself no longer. She didn't dare risk being seen in a local bakery so she took the bus to the next town. Nobody from her home village came here to shop. Nevertheless, she glanced guiltily to left and right before venturing into Crawford's, The Bakers.

Five minutes later Alice crouched in deserted sand dunes, her collar turned up to ward off the December chill. In that moment all thoughts of *Massachusetts* and anticipation of the wedding evaporated. She seized the steaming sausage roll from its greasy paper bag. She bit off a chunk. She closed her eyes. The taste and smell of the seasoned meat saturated her senses. Flakes of pastry landed like confetti on the front of her coat. A dream come true.

Shona Montgomery

Diet? Thought I might try it

No dinner, feel thinner
skip supper, less blubber
lose pounds, less round
no chips, see my hips
less fries, firmer thighs
chew gum, smaller bum
smother appetite, death to cellulite.

Celery stalks, plenty of walks
baked tatties, then Pilates
pulses and beans, keep me lean
5-a-day, what a buffet
vegetables? indigestibles
fresh or tinned, but, oh, the wind!
passing phase, lasted 3 days.

Stuart Blair

The Farewell Dinner

Kate, who had recently retired from teaching, and her husband, Josh, had been invited to a farewell dinner at Danai and Felix's home. For the last month the two men had been medical colleagues at the one hundred bed Mission Hospital in Murumbinda. Danai was employed as one of the hospital's pharmacists. The other two guests were Thabane, also a doctor at the hospital and his wife, Vimbai, the senior pharmacist working there. The Zimbabweans were in their early thirties and climbing ladders professionally while Kate and Josh, the Scots, had retired from such pursuits.

The dinner invitation was one with a twist, for Kate had been asked to cook the main and only dish, a request that she had not expected since she and her husband were the ones who were leaving the following day to go on safari before returning home. She wondered if her hosts thought that she might cook a course with a Scottish twist. In truth, because of the scarcity of food, whatever she produced would consist of ingredients that were available.

As Kate had never visited Mutare, she and her husband took a trip there the day before they were due to have the meal. For nearly two hours they travelled cheek by jowl with the locals in a boneshaker of a bus. Before they returned to Murumbinda, they scrabbled around at the bottom of one of the freezers in a supermarket in the town's centre and found a pack of scraggy meat which would be enough for six.

Cooking the food was challenging for Kate as there was only a Baby Belling cooker at her disposal in the students' bungalow, the only accommodation available. One of the cooker's two rings did not function. It seemed incongruous to her that they had been given such spartan accommodation when Josh had been invited to take on the role of Chief Medical Officer for a month, on a voluntary basis, to allow the incumbent employee time to visit her family in South Africa.

The stew which she concocted was enhanced with onions, cinnamon, cumin and a small bottle of red wine. While it was braising, a splendid aroma wafted round the kitchen-cum-living room. It was all the more intoxicating because neither Kate nor Josh had eaten meat or chicken for the last month as there was none on sale in the local store. Occasionally, chickens' feet were available, but these were meant for dogs. What happened to the other parts of the chickens was a puzzle for they were never on offer. The supermarket's shelves and the market's stalls were always half empty as a result of the political unrest caused by Mugabe's regime. One day the couple ate courgettes and tomatoes and the next they had tomatoes and courgettes. Sometimes, this was accompanied by eggs, baked beans, onions or greens. Like everyone else, sadza was their staple and always obtainable. Variety was not the name of the game. Having a small amount of sustenance was.

The couple walked carefully along the gravel track from their house to that of their hosts' home, inside the hospital compound, carrying the precious food which was still in the pots. As they passed the maternity ward they heard the women chanting in the melancholy way that was customary immediately after a baby's death. Life was cheap in those parts and a baby dying was a common occurrence.

When Kate and Josh reached the bungalow, they were greeted warmly by Danai. Kate was taken aback by her hostess's stunning appearance for she was wearing bright pink, stiletto-heeled shoes, a pair of tight, fashionable, navy jeans and a purple shirt with long sleeves, all of which showed off her slim figure beautifully. Added to that, a purple hair piece decorated her long, wiry, black hair. Obviously, she had made an effort to look glamorous. Kate on the other hand, was in a sand-coloured shift frock and Jesus sandals, both of which had seen better days. She felt self-conscious and irritated at herself for she had made assumptions that were wrong.

'You look lovely, Danai,' said Kate. 'I didn't expect to be going out for dinner on this trip. My apologies. I should have packed something dressier.' She ran her fingers down her frock as if to take out imaginary creases.

31

'You are a beautiful person on the inside which is far more important,' Danai said as she ushered her guests into the kitchen.

Kate entered it first. She was taken aback at the sight of a hen and her clutch of chickens in a cage on the floor of the larder. Clumsily, she laid the heavy, cast-iron pot of stew on the cooker. As if they had been fired out of a rifle, dozens of cockroaches scuttled across the worktop in a frenzy. Stifling a gasp, she glanced at her husband as he laid down the other two pots. Looking in Kate's direction, he pursed his lips. The message was clear. *Say nothing.*

'Sorry about all the roaches,' said Danai nervously.

'We should be apologising to you, Danai,' said Josh. 'Yesterday, I learned from the administrator that you two were due to have your home fumigated before our bungalow was done, but you said you'd wait until after we'd left. That was generous of you.'

'You and Kate were going to be doing enough in coming to work out here with us. Nobody wanted you to put up with roaches as well. Once you get them, it is difficult to get rid of them. We are used to them.'

'I didn't know about this,' said Kate. 'That was really kind.'

'Thanks for being so understanding about them,' said Danai. 'Come into the lounge.'

Felix, Thabane and Vimbai were sitting in comfortable armchairs. Vimbai was dressed in a similar outfit to Danai and she, too, wore a purple hair piece. The three of them were chatting in Shona, a language of which Kate had little knowledge. Josh, however, could understand and use some words and phrases. As soon as the three of them saw the couple, they spoke in English as they always did when they were in the company of the two Scots.

On seeing the armchairs, Kate had a deep need to slip into one of them for their accommodation had no seats other than two kitchen chairs. After greeting the others, she sat down in one of the seats. Her body sank into the upholstery with each bone and muscle slowly relaxing one by one or so it seemed. Momentarily, she closed her eyes and took some deep breaths. Until an hour ago, she had been packing up their belongings, cleaning and cooking while the outside temperature hovered at around thirty-four degrees which was tiring, particularly when there was no air conditioning. There was air conditioning in this bungalow. What joy!

After enjoying a pre-dinner glass of wine, they took their places at the dining table at the far end of the room. Once seated at the table, Danai brought through plates of the steaming stew accompanied by the rice and greens. Kate basked in the glory of the compliments about the food. By then, she had forgotten about the cockroaches or, to put it differently, she was ignoring what she had seen.

The conversation flowed easily while everyone ate. It was when her fork was raised with the last mouthful of beef on it that, out of the corner of her eye, Kate caught sight of something moving above the number twelve on the metal rim of the large, circular clock on the wall in front of her. Since starting to eat, darkness had fallen and the room was dimly lit with only candles on the table. Kate screwed up her eyes and focussed on the object once more. There it was again. Something was fluttering. She peered. A large, bright green and black striped insect about eight centimetres long was perched on the rim. Its protruding black eyes seemed to penetrate Kate's.

Vimbai asked her a question, but she did not respond. She sat motionless. They all looked at the clock to see what was holding her attention.

'Just a grasshopper,' said Thabane, sitting next to Kate.

She nodded. As she slipped the food into her mouth, the grasshopper opened its wings and flew towards her. Its wings were iridescent. She ducked, but she was too late. The creature landed on top of her auburn hair. It struggled to free itself while simultaneously making an angry buzzing sound. Kate sat still, not even blinking. She swallowed hard.

'I will remove it for you. Do not be frightened,' said Thabane as he disentangled the grasshopper from her hair. With its torso between his thumb and forefinger, he placed it on the table and then held it down by putting his thumb on its back. This insect was going nowhere, at least not for the moment. Without saying a word, he dismembered it and placed its limbs on the side of his empty plate.

'I'm not frightened. I don't like the idea of large insects in my hair, though.' Kate shuddered. She was too polite to tell Thabane that she did not like him pulling the legs off the insect unnecessarily.

Thabane placed the creature's limbs on the edge of his plate. 'Would you eat it?' He wore a puzzled expression on his face.

'Me? I don't know. I've never tried one. Do you eat these?' asked Kate.

'Of course. They are so special.'

'You have to remember that tonight we are lucky. We go to bed with stomachs full of nutritious, tasty food, but many of our people might only have had sadza,' said Felix. 'These insects provide protein and, what is more, they are very tasty.'

'I understand.'

'Our children climb the trees to collect them,' he continued. 'They eat them raw. The adults fry them in oil to make a relish. It is a delicacy. A most wonderful delicacy.' As he spoke his eyes lit up and he pretended to swoon.

Kate stared at the grasshopper. An angry, buzzing sound emanated from it. Its torso twirled on the spot, before slowly coming to a standstill.

'Here, let me take everyone's plate?' Danai said cheerfully as if to move on from the subject. When collecting the plates, she also picked up the grasshopper's body.

While waiting for her plate to be removed a thought came into Kate's mind and when there was a break in the conversation, she said, 'I would like to return to the subject of grasshoppers.' A quick glance at Josh told her that he was apprehensive about what she was going to say, but she carried on.

'Before I came out here, I remember learning on a TV programme that some African countries might be well on their way to showing the rest of the world how protein from some insects could be used if nations reared them in sufficient quantities to provide sustenance that would make a difference. An expert told us that mopane worms are a great source of nourishment, especially in this country.'

'They are,' said Vimbai, 'the best delicacy,' much tastier and meatier than grasshoppers. We eat them in our homes and in restaurants. In some of the high-class restaurants in Harare, they are, how do you say it, a signature dish.'

There was silence at the table. The clicking sound of male cicadas could be heard in the nearby trees. The women had stopped singing for the child who had died.

'A signature dish. Perhaps, if we return, you might cook some mopane worms for us. I may have retired, but I have a lot to learn,' Kate replied.

Felix picked up his glass. 'A toast to our friends, Kate and Josh. Have a good journey home and 'Hasha ye kudzoka' or to say this in your language, 'Haste ye back.''

Kate and Josh sat back in their chairs and smiled.

Brenda Thomson

'How are you?' 'I'm fine'

I was in Sudan, part of a British Council teacher training team. We were there to introduce English teachers to a new English course.* Early on one of the teachers we were training invited me to visit his school. He introduced me to his class.

'Ask them what their parents do,' he suggested.

'What does your father do?' I asked a boy sitting in the front.

'My father is a postman,' he replied promptly.

'And your mother?'

'My mother is a dressmaker.'

'And you?' I asked the boy next to him.

'My father is a postman and my mother is a dressmaker' he replied equally promptly.

I soon realised that if it was true what they were saying there were 40 postmen and 40 dressmakers in the village. What we were there for was to introduce them to a way of teaching English based on real communication. Instead of having the whole class reciting given phrases in chorus as in the teaching of the Koran we'd have them turning to each other and having real conversations. 'Work in pairs,' we told them. 'Turn to your neighbour and practise the following dialogue: 'How are you?' 'I'm fine. And you?' 'I'm fine too.'

One Friday towards the end of the course they invited us to a picnic by the Nile. My notion of a picnic – a wicker basket containing cucumber sandwiches and a thermos of tea – was to receive a rude cultural jolt. They'd brought a live sheep along.

'We will kill it before your eyes and then we will eat it,' one of the students informed me.

A short while later, as an honoured guest, I found myself being offered the choicest titbits – raw liver and lungs still steaming from having been inside the living sheep. It was mid morning, hardly a time to be eating meat, but at no time during the day or night could I have faced eating raw liver and lungs. What was I to do? I was a lapsed Catholic but the Church served me well on this occasion. In the Catholic Church Friday used to be a day of abstinence when eating meat was forbidden. 'I'm sorry but my religion forbids me from eating meat on a Friday,' I told them in a tone of deep regret. As devout Muslims they immediately understood the strictures that religion imposed.

But this meant I wasn't able to eat the delicious bits of the sheep either. Instead, as we lay under the trees, chatting and drinking glasses of abundantly sugared mint tea, I ate grapes and dates and little cakes. 'How are you?' we'd ask each other. 'I'm fine. And you?' 'I'm fine too.' Towards evening a group of women passed, greeting us cheerily.

'We would like to have spent the whole day with you,' they sang out.

I have a lovely memory of that picnic by the Nile.

I'm thinking of it now as I read about the terrible events happening in Sudan, the army and the rival paramilitary Rapid Support Forces in armed conflict, fighting it out for power with no care for the civilian population in their midst. Hospitals are being bombed and schools and dwellings. The UN estimates that more than a million people have been displaced, many perishing in the process. A quarter of a million have fled across the borders into Chad, Ethiopia, Egypt, South Sudan. How welcome are they there, South Sudan the poorest country in the world? I think of that day, of that picnic by the Nile. 'How are you?' I'm fine. And you? . . .'

Olivia McMahon

* *'The NILE Course' by Martin Bates*

Feeding the Monster

Parked in front of the row of open-hearth furnaces, he could feel the heat, and perhaps also the hate directed at the Boss's son. It was called 'getting shop floor experience'. Neil was learning how to fettle the beasts using a special shovel: the great doors were opened a fraction, and the fettler had to direct a stream of refractory material straight through the gap in a horizontal line, until it hit the back of the furnace, without being licked up by the hungry flames. You had to get it just right. One of the melters was a huge Pole, even though it was well before the Second World War, and the Polish Embassy had only just opened.

'First time you get it wrong, I show you. Second time, I tell you. Third time, I pick you up and throw you in furnace!' A joke, but only just.

Three classes of melter worked the furnaces – first hand melter, second hand melter, third hand melter. A first hand melter had a good wage, a fair portion of which went on ale – a melter could sweat six pints in a shift, easy. And shift not a few 'dripping butties' at break times. There were others working in the melting shop, but a first-hand melter was king, with the two crane drivers next in pecking order. The melters were at the cutting edge of technology, with ore quantities, temperatures, everything recorded in little ledgers.

Neil was glad when the shift ended. While he tried to join in the jokes and camaraderie, it was awkward; they all knew it. It was easier spending a night shift with a crane driver, learning the rhythm of the steel-making process; riding the roof of the melting shop, picking up an empty ladle, carrying it to the mouth of a furnace before it poured, and a golden gleam of molten steel streamed and splashed into the ladle. On top of the hot metal, a pool of slag formed. A burn from hot steel was always better than slag; if it didn't kill you outright a slag injury was dirty and never healed.

He knew that the name came from a village in Yorkshire – Slack – and originally meant trodden down, but now it meant either dirty residue or a woman. Men were never called slags. How unfair names were, not least when the blast furnaces which produced the pig iron for the steel furnaces were named after the four English Queens – Mary, Bess, Anne and Victoria. Life was unfair – he could see what was going on in the late Nineteen-Twenties, and he did not see eye to eye with his father.

The five furnaces in their shop were all called after Greek monsters – females again! – his Scottish grandfather had known the Classics – so here were Scylla, Typhon, Lammy, the Gorgon, and the Cherub. Where did the Cherub come from? Well, you couldn't expect a Sheffield melter to cope with Charybdis. And Lammy? That was Lamia, a child-eating monster. Neil's mind wandered. Did the steel industry feed the world without cost? What about the accidents, the children left fatherless? Did his grandfather ever read about the Hunger Marches?

The crane driver was friendly, but knew which side his bread was buttered; and stuck to his job of teaching the young master what he could. How the ladle in turn would pour the hot steel into moulds, forming huge ingots which glowed dull scarlet with digested heat, braced for passage through the body of the works, to be deposited at a rolling mill which reduced the ingot to a bar; then to a bar mill, and other processes. There was hot rolling and cold rolling, and all kinds of products could be made, from steel rails to rods for reinforced concrete. With five mills, four ladles, and two cranes, things had to be done in good order – ladles were hungry, and hot steel could not easily wait.

One kind of mill gripped his imagination – the wire mill. A rod would be reheated, then put into the wire mill. It would go in slow, but as it was reduced in diameter it would come out faster and faster as it became wire, Recently, a few safety features had been introduced, but he knew that in the old days a 'catcher' would be employed to grab the wire with a pair of tongs and turn it rapidly round a stob so that it went into the right channel. There were horror stories of what happened when the mill went wild and red-hot wire went flying through the air . . .

All this was part of imperial Britain, part of how you fed an Empire to keep it alive. The red parts of the map all had to be supplied with steel products. He had been brought up to believe in Empire, and he had swallowed it, like his father before him, but sometimes he wondered. The red was cooling in his mind, rather like an ingot left too long on its own before passing into the next part of the process. What was the point of it all? Where would it end? Was the world a giant factory, where an ingot could be reduced to a rod, a rod to wire, a wire to a paper clip so that someone, somewhere could pin a country in its place? Was Britain feeding products to Africa and Asia? What about the iron ore which fed the blast furnaces, and the open-hearth melting shop in turn? Was the Empire feeding Britain? Over the years, it formed something of a feeding frenzy in his mind.

* * *

Ten years later, it was 1939, and Europe was on the brink of war.

Neil was now Personnel Director, and took his job seriously. The works were a bit safer than back in 1929. The politicians kept saying that peace would prevail, but Neil had his ear to the ground. He got on well with the men, not least a few from Eastern Europe. He knew more about the mind of Hitler than Neville Chamberlain. But he was liable for call-up if war was to come.

His older brother Charles was Managing Director. They had never been close. Neil was not happy about the way Charles ran things. As the year went on, the Government changed and Britain did declare war. Extra steel was needed for armaments, and Charles put up prices. At one Board meeting Neil called it profiteering. The rest of the Board just sat there, stoney-faced, while the Chairman (their father) quickly passed on to other business. Neil thought of them all as 'the Stonies'.

Charles escaped call-up because of his key position, but Neil spent six years as an officer with the Argylls. A bit strange that, you would have expected him to join a local regiment. But he had, like his brother, been at a Scottish public school, and his connections were with the Argyll and Sutherland Highlanders. However, the Second World War (so-called) is not really part of this story, except that it took Neil off the scene for all that time.

Meanwhile the firm prospered. Charles went all out for the production needed to meet the war effort. Like other manufacturers in wartime, he cut corners, kept old equipment going the best he could, with little regard for safety. Of course, accidents did happen, but nothing which attracted attention until just before the end of the War. Charles and his father were in the works when a ladle burst, and the molten slag caught them. The old man died outright from the shock of it, Charles lived for a week. Others died too, but the papers had a long article praising the family for what they had done 'to feed the war effort through five years of horror'.

Neil had tried to pick up the pieces after the accident, they had appointed someone else as Managing Director, and Neil had become Chairman of the Board. After the war, in November 1949, the industry was nationalized by the Labour Government's Iron and Steel Act, but this was reversed by the Conservatives in 1951. Life was not easy. Neil had always taken a very basic view of his task; to employ people to make a vital product and to pay them a wage which would let them feed their children properly. But he had also to make enough money to invest in a company whose methods were old-fashioned and was now threatened by more efficient overseas competitors like Hoogovens in the Netherlands.

Neil was still there in 1959. By this time, open-hearth melting shops were beginning to feel the pressure from the cheaper and faster electric arc furnace, but the five monsters were still producing steel, still being fettled, still being fed with a mixture of iron ore and other materials. Over the next eight years he did his best to keep things good for customers and workers, and also the family, though by this time their share-holding was diluted and employees had a seat on the Board; unusual in those days outside of the great Quaker factory families.

* * *

It was now the end of July 1967. Harold Wilson's Iron and Steel Act had just gone through Parliament and been approved by the Queen, a second attempt at putting the British Steel industry into public hands.

That night, Neil had a very strange dream. He was standing as a young man in front of Nebuchadnezzar's fiery furnace, along with Daniel's three young men – only they were three melters, one from India, one from Kenya, one from Poland. Daniel, not the Babylonian tyrant, was in charge of the furnace, and he raised the furnace door. The flames streamed out towards him. The Pole handed him a shovel. He picked up a load of fettling material and flung it at the furnace. Suddenly, the flames went out. The monster could no longer eat.

The next day Neil stepped down as Chair. Before he left his office, he replied to a letter which had been sitting in his in-tray for weeks. It was from Oxfam, inviting him to join their Board of Trustees.

Jock Stein

Food Rationing

Following World War II eggs were still rationed, and when they were scarce there was only one per person per week. My mum remembers going into the country and being sent into a small holding to ask if they had any eggs for sale. Sometimes she got two, occasionally more. These eggs were tuppence each. In Summer when eggs were more plentiful my grandmother would pickle them in isinglass.

On Sunday, for a treat, because there were no cakes to buy, my grandmother would let my mum make vanilla slices – two cream crackers with a little custard inside and a smear of icing on top.

At school, my mum and her friends were always hoping for air-raid warnings. They then had to go out to the shelters in the school grounds and wait for the all-clear. They carried their gas-masks everywhere and would often eat their packed lunch in the shelter.

Driving at night was quite frightening. Cars were only allowed masked headlights which were very dim. Once, on the way home from visiting his brother, my grandfather got lost and the family ended up in a river outside Dalkeith.

My mum and her friends would go to Queensferry to see the huge silver balloons which protected the Forth Bridge. They went armed with jam pieces and orange juice.

Food was scarce but the family always had potatoes and bread and never went hungry. My grandfather used to get hares from friends who lived in the country. My grandmother made hare soup which my mum hated but had to eat because in those days it was take it or leave it, there was nothing else on offer.

My mum was delighted, when in 1953, the rationing of sweets and chocolate came to an end. To the day she died my mum always had a 'sweetie' drawer full of biscuits and chocolate bars just in case she got any visitors.

Nova Brown

The Walk to the Shop

The children set off from a small bungalow at the end of the road. Between them, one handle each, they carry a sturdy bag made of brown leather. Within it are a purse, a shopping list and a ration book. They head up the road towards the pit village where there is a shop they call 'The Store'. They are proud to be trusted with the job of getting the messages.

The boy is about 8 years old and the girl two years younger. She is wearing a skirt that has been made from a tweed coat that belonged to someone bigger and a matted fair-isle jumper. The boy is wearing short trousers and a brown jerkin with sleeves that are too short. A little way up the street they stop to speak to a cat that is sitting in the small front garden of a house very similar to their own. It refuses to come and be stroked. It blinks its eyes and yawns before sprawling full-length on the unkempt grass. They leave the houses behind and pass between the fields on either side of the road. Soon they reach the village where winding gear and coal dust dominate the small cluster of streets.

The Store is a big stone building and inside there is a central space with counters all around it. The walls are covered in white tiles and the floor in stone slabs. They head for the counter where a barrel shape of butter sits on a marble slab. The boy hands the shopping list to the woman behind the counter who takes up a large knife, cuts out a small piece of butter and slaps it onto the piece of paper sitting on the scales. She smiles at the children.

'Give me the ration book then.'

They hand over the book and watch as she carefully tears out the coupons. Then they hand over the purse and the shop-lady takes out a couple of silver coins and puts some coppers back in the purse.

'Your Mam alright?'

They nod.

'Your Dad still away?'

They nod again and say thank you politely before going to the next counter where a side of bacon is sitting beside a slicing machine. Three thin slices are wrapped in another piece of greaseproof paper. They move on to the cheese counter where a small piece of cheese is cut from a larger slab. Then they hand over the list to the man behind a counter in front of a row of wooden shelves.

'2 tins of beans. Tomato soup. Rich Tea biscuits.' Then the man shovels some loose tea into a brown paper bag, weighs it, and folds over the top. 'That's the lot,' he says, 'can you manage?'

The children nod and carefully put their precious purchases and the almost empty purse into the bag. They set off back down the road slowly. The bag is heavier than on the way up. They stop to speak to a horse in a field and put down the bag as it comes over to them. They smile at each other.

Lorna Dixon

Interlude

The following three pieces were submitted through STAND (Stronger Together for Autism and Neurodivergence), an organisation based in Tranent and partnered by Tyne and Esk Writers. They are written by young people who benefit from the work of STAND.

Chocolate Orange Prime

KSI (JJ) and Logan Paul like mixing
weird things with chocolate.
His favourite chocolate is light chocolate.
He also invents PRIME.
He is going to invent a chocolate orange
Prime drink. It's a meta
moon type prime, 'hydration', 500ml.
Hydration means no fizz. Its
bottle is brown, orange, and blue. The
liquid inside is brown too.
It's flavoured chocolate orange with real
chocolate and real orange.
It will probably sell out because it will be
so popular.

Jaxon (age 12)

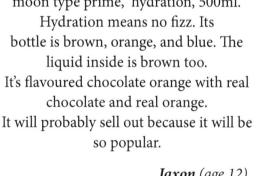

Editor's Note: Jaxon used a design
which we have had to recast, and we
apologise for this. Sorry Jaxon, this is
not as good as yours was (in colour)!

Banana Magic

One day in Gorilla Tag, there was a lava gorilla, and it was trying to infect every gorilla with the lava infection, so anyone the lava gorilla touch turn into lava gorillas! But after years of lava gorillas, a gorilla rose from the forest with millions of bananas and handed them out to all lava gorillas and had a banana party with bananas and lots more bananas that all of the gorillas ate. The end.

Arran (age 12)

My Favourite Food

I like lettuce and so does Claud, a tortoise. One day in chicken burger town, there was a giant tortoise stealing the chicken burgers lettuce! ! And the tortoise army is planning on harvesting all of the lettuce and eat it all, then become chunky and strong to be able to take over the planet and rename it Tortoise Shell Citadel. But the chicken burgers had created a de-shelling device which weakens the tortoise. But a siren started and it said "5-4-3-2-1- war has started!" Then, the chicken burgers brought out the de-tortoise bomb and it exploded! All of the chicken burgers took their lettuce back and celebrated their victory! The chicken burgers were never bothered again. The end.

Arran (age 12)

Scurries' Aigs

I aye rase withoot being telt tae
faan we bid at Grandad's in e simmer.
At five years auld, I sat at e table,
twa cushions unner me
an Grandad across frae me
wytin, wytin, wytin
fur e scurries' aigs tae be brocht
through in thir widen cups –
bonnie, spraiklt an broon,
a hint o blue in a puckle.

I'd tap mine wi ma been speen,
lift aff e tap gently an see a splurge
o bricht, rinny orange an smell e sea.
'A speeshal trait fur you,' said Grandad,
winkin an smilin at me.

He hid scramblt doon e scaars,
pluckt e aigs frae neests
on e ledges at e Bullers o Buchan,
pit maist in his cannas shooder bag
an e rist ooner his flat caip,
aa fur me.

Glossary: *scurries* – seagulls, *aigs* – *eggs*, rase – *rose*, *faan* – *when*, bid –
stayed, *simmer* – summer, *auld* – old, *wytin* – waiting, *spraiklt* – speckled,
a puckle – some, *been* – bone, *speen* – spoon, *bricht* – bright, trait – treat,
scaars – cliffs, *speeshal* – special, *neests* – nests. *maist* – most, *caanas* –
canvas, *shooder* – shoulder, *rist* – rest, *ooner* – under, *caip* – cap, *aa* – all

Brenda Thomson

Farms Encircling Tranent in the '50s

The East Lothian Co-op owned farms of eleven hundred fertile acres which encircled Tranent from Elphinstone to Macmerry. West Windygoul was a vegetable farm. The manager was Mr Hunt. Geordie Henderson, Davy Henderson and George Jamieson were tractor drivers. Willie Bailey drove a pair of black Belgian horses. His tall, gaunt father, also Willie Bailey, owned Whiteloch Farm at Macmerry. In 1956, he told me that his father had run a regular service with teams of horses pulling an open *charabanc* from Musselburgh to Tranent prior to motor buses.

A mile from the town centre there were several disused air shafts which had once ventilated pit workings. I helped the shepherd to throw dead sheep down these shafts. The shale, from the disused Fleets Colliery bings, was used to fill them in.

In the mid-forties, during rationing, employees were allowed, unofficially, to buy a quarter pound of margarine from the Co-op where they worked. In the mid-fifties, however, some Co-op members stole goods and equipment from the Society farms and shops. The Co-op was the property of the working class. It was built by dint of members efforts. As a teenager who has always felt part of the decent working class, I was deeply dismayed.

Mr Hunt, who had been gassed during the war, also ran the tomato glasshouses at Bank Park which employed Alec Paton, George Brown and some ladies.

When I started to work on the farm at East Windygoul in the Spring of 1955, we used a railway bag as a raincoat by turning one bottom corner into another when hit with April showers. In summer my brown hair was bleached blond at the front by the sunshine.

The manager for East Windygoul, Kingslaw, Muirpark, and Adniston Farms, all of which were arable, was Tom McMillan. The steward was George Smith at East Windygoul, the foreman (or first horseman) was Duncan Jack. The second horsemen, over time, were Jocky Brown, Bob Seton and finally Willie McCabe. The first three horsemen reaped and sowed and ploughed and mowed all the fields of crops.

The twenty years old Seton twins, George and Bob, arrived around 1950 at East Windygoul Farm with their Mum, Dad and younger sister Agnes, a bonnie, bubbly twelve-year-old. Both were accomplished players of complex mouth organs. George, fair-haired, gentle with a droll sense of humour and an intelligent twinkle in his eye, drove a green Fordson tractor. Bob was dark haired, lean, gregarious and macho with a raucous laugh. His primary pursuits were his farm craftsmanship and attractive ladies. Bob's horses were Sandy and Star. Sandy would sink his teeth into the shoulders of anyone who entered his stall, lifting them off the ground.

The potato field at the Balderstrip had been sown with wheat. Bob followed on with his two horses and four leaves of heavy harrows covering the seed. To clear the debris from his harrows, he lifted a leaf and urged his horses forward a step. The harrow slipped from his grasp! Two six-inch pointed steel tines of the harrows shot through his rubber wellington boots. Bob passed out and fell forward across the harrows with his head lying between the steel shoes of Star's hooves. His horses stood stock still. As Duncan Jack held him Frankie Purves cut his wellington boots from his feet. Both harrow tines had rammed down between Bob's toes with not a graze was to be seen. Bob was given to moments of pointless rage. It was always his horses to blame, never Bob. He was given the third pair at the Myles Farm, one of whom was a fine dapple-grey Clydesdale named Pride. Farmer Dykes sacked Bob for sinking his boot into this horse's belly.

The third pair at East Windygoul, Prince and Paddy, were driven by William Wallace, a pleasant, slim, fellow with a David Niven moustache, who left to take up fencing with his dad, Jake Wallace. Paddy went to Adniston Farm. Prince pulled the cart which delivered the miners' concessionary coal in Ormiston. The succession of odd-horse (single horse) drivers were Dave Bathgate, Jackie Stevenson, Will McNeill, Tommy Henderson, Jimmy Jamieson, Davy Burnett, Jimmy Parker, Jock McNeill, Bobby Henderson and me.

FRONT ROW (MS - NOT KNOWN) JOSIE STEPHENSON WITH (?)
JEANIE JAMES, BESSIE BATHGATE 2ND ROW MEG JACK, AGNES
SETON, BOB SETON BACK ARTHUR GREENAN

The ladies who worked in the fields were Meg Jack, Bessie Bathgate, Jenny Wilson, Annie Cross, Mary Ross, Kate Clapperton, Margaret Reilly, Josie Stephenson, Jeanie James and Mima Kerr. The ladies' gaffer was Jock Renton, who sported a fine, slim military moustache and no teeth. The tractor drivers were George Seton and Murdo Smith, now with new blue Fords, and Eck Hogg with an aged, dark green Fordson. The shepherd was Bob Dickson who had an ancient orange Allis Chalmers.

There were two pairs of horses, a Belgian pair driven by Mark Burns, plus a pair of Clydesdales, Jock and Billy, which were driven by Frankie McCabe. When I was three years old, these two ploughmen stopped their two pairs of horses in the field that they were ploughing at the foot of our garden at Muirpark Terrace to have their breakfast. Unseen, I scrambled through the boundary wire fence and walked under Mark's Burn's two horses then under Frankie McCabes's pair. As I tried to lift the horses off the ground, Frankie dived between his horses' hooves to rescue me.

Mark's Belgian pair were replaced by two dapple-grey Percherons which, a few years later, were replaced by a pair of young Clydesdale mares which were far too skittish for Mark Burns to control.

WILLIE McCABE (JNR), ECK HOGG, MARK BURNS, MURDO
SMITH, MRS X?, JOCK RENTON, DUNCAN JACK, WILLIE
ROBERTSON, GEORDIE SMITH AND MEG JACK 1953

The red, 'International Farmall' tractor was driven by Frank Purves; then, on his emigration to Australia, by Hugh McLeod (Sen). That tractor had two tapered front wheels for use in the turnip rows and potato drills. As old Hughie turned into Muirpark Farm a lorry whipped the front wheels off it.

Muirpark Farm was staffed from the other farms. The fattening cattle, which were mainly Hereford bullocks, were fed throughout the winter by the crippled cattle man, Bob White, who had fought in Mesopotamia after WW1. He helped the vet to remove their horns with a blood-spattered hacksaw. The antiseptic was pure *Dettol* squirted on the wound from an oil pourrie.

DUNCAN JACK, WILLIE MCCABE, (SEN), MR X ?,
MARK BURNS, JOCK RENTON. WINTON CASTLE 1949

Adniston Farm in 1955 was self-contained. Wattie Wilson, a pleasant man, was the grieve, and the foreman was Tom Black, known as 'Red Mick' because of his florid complexion and his socialist views. The second pair of Clydesdales were driven by Jimmy Anderson, the third by Johnnie Boyd and the odd horse, which was a Suffolk Punch, by Ian Muir. The tractor drivers were Dod Nisbet and Bobby Rae, the cattleman was Bob Jamieson and the orra men were Ninian Wightman and Dod Shiel. The ladies who worked there were Mrs Wilson, a kindly woman who was the wife of Wattie, Mrs Rae, Mrs Jamieson, Mrs Anderson and Mrs Shiel. Wattie Wilson had a cousin, Walter Wilson, who was about to get married when he received his call up papers for WW1. In an act of supreme courage and decency, Wattie Wilson, who was younger and single, took his cousin Walter's place.

The ladies, on cold winter days, kept me alive with their barley sugar sweeties. I am pleased to remember them. Walter Wilson, the cousin of the farm steward, became the woman's gaffer.

Farmworkers Union 1955

I was taken to a Union meeting where I was enrolled into the Agricultural Section of The Transport and General Workers Union, once enchantingly known as the Scottish Horse and Motormen's Union. The branch Secretary, Johnnie Paton from Riggonhead Farm, requested that I be appointed as his assistant. My task was to cycle around the farms in the eastern part of the county once a month, to collect the union dues from the enlisted members. I set off on my new Raleigh three-speed bicycle which I had bought from Petersen's in Musselburgh. The Hire Purchase Terms then were that I should pay a £2 deposit and twenty-four weeks repayment at £1 per week! The transfer on the crossbar read Vox Populi which translated as *the voice of the people.*

DUNCAN JACK AT HADDINGTON SHOW
WITH HIS PRIZE CLYDESDALE GELDING

Arriving at Ormiston North Mains Farm, Mrs White, the cattleman's wife, an elegant woman, had the jam scones and wedding-crockery ready. They were an elderly, childless couple, who were so civilized that they represented my true heroes in this world, the well-to-do working class.

In stark contrast, in the next cottage, there lived a family of four grown sons with their Northern Irish parents. The sons, all of whom worked on the farm and in their twenties, were gentle lads with ready smiles. When I, as an unworldly fifteen-year-old, was asked to meet their father, I entered their house assuming he wanted to join the Union.

I was hit with a barrage of incessant putrefaction by their father, Mr Allan. This ugly little man, like his hero the Reverend Dr Ian Paisley, bordered on insanity. My understanding, then, of Mr Allan's troubled background in Northern Ireland, was nil.

His appreciation of our brotherly spirit in East Lothian of 'We're a' Jock Tamson's Bairns' was nil, too. That June, 1956, the Queen visited Tranent and accepted a posy of flowers from my wee sister, Magdalen, who was the town's Gala queen. I then sped off to Lennoxlove Estate to the Annual Show of livestock. I saw Tom Macmillan, being presented with a perpetual silver trophy for exhibiting the best Friesian heifer in the show. Kingslaw was a large dairy farm. The senior dairyman was Bob McMaster, aided by his wife, Jimmy Little and Willie Robertson. It supplied the milk to the bottling plant at the Central Co-op. With the trophy went a silver pint tankard as a memento of the achievement.

In 1966, I met Tom again who was, by now, an aged man. One summer's evening, I took him for a trip across the Moorfoot Hills to the farm of Mount Benger. We met the shepherd, Ally Murray whose predecessor there was James Hogg, known as the 'Ettrick Shepherd' who was a literary soulmate of Robbie Burns. That evening we repaired to the nearby Gordon Arms Hotel near St Mary's Loch.

It was enchanting for a young man like me to sit quietly back and listen to these two experienced stockmen as they swapped their stories and sunk nips with great speed. I returned Tom safely to his house. He kindly gave me the souvenir pint tankard which the Queen had presented to him at Haddington Show for exhibiting the Best Friesian Heifer in the Show. As a simple-minded country laddie I was, and still am, touched by his thoughtfulness.

Arthur Greenan

The Breeching Party

After church, the new apprentice, Roger Seager, walked with his master back down the earthen track to the mill house. When they arrived, Miller Flight took off his pattens and hung his justacorps and tricorn hat on wooden pegs in the hall. He ushered Roger into the parlour and positioned himself close to the hearth where a coal fire was warming the room. He looked every part a gentleman in his fine clothes: a fancy yellow jabot to offset a pale blue waistcoat, black breeches, yellow hose and black polished shoes. Roger stood, hands clasped behind his back, by the big well-scrubbed table on which there were piles of decorated plates, and a great many knives, pewter tankards and glass goblets, and two bottles of smuggled brandy provided by his master.

While he waited for Charlie and his guests, Miller Flight was thinking about his own breeching party. He said to Roger that he had felt half-known by his father, a bosun on a sailing ship, away for weeks at a time, but he remembered how important it had been for that sailor to bring his son into the world of men; 'Just like every good father in England'. Flight said that was why he had offered his millhand Charlie the use of the parlour for Danny's party. 'Charlie's a good man and wants the best for his boy. My own son, David, was breeched in this very room and quickly learned the mill work but he said it was not for him and he joined the Royal Navy. I required much from him and he is a lieutenant now, sailing to the West Indies under Vice-Admiral Benbow. If God spares him, he will be a captain one day.'

Roger said that he remembered feeling so proud to get out of wearing a childish dress and the miller nodded. Then in the silence, save for the sparking of the fire, Roger's unshared memories were about the hard adjustment that followed his breeching: his father's sharp demand for skilfulness with the tools, his disregard of tears when a chisel sliced a finger and a skelp whenever Roger's attention wandered from the task in hand.

He had struggled to understand men-talk about conflict and women and righteousness and had blushed when they laughed at his attempts to join in. Roger reckoned that every man found it a hard journey.

There was a knock and the miller went to open the big front door. Roger wondered about the years ahead, of God's requirement that he convert from woodturner's son to miller. How had the master become such a grand fellow? Flight was the richest man Roger had met, wealthy because of many accomplishments – miller, merchant, manager of men. Would it not be lonely, maintaining a social distance and business-like demeaner in all his dealings with other men?

Within moments, Miller Flight had returned with Charlie, his wife Betty and their children, Danny and Alice, who looked like sisters in brown woollen dresses, thin bare ankles underneath and tangled hair hanging over their shoulders. Charlie thanked master Flight again for the use of his parlour, and for the brandy, then went to give Roger a friendly thump on the shoulder. They talked quietly about the mill work and Betty held and whispered to her children.

By and by their guests also came in: the other millhands, three bargemen and two fishermen, all with their wives; the baker, his wife and dozen other villagers, most with children of their own. The men, Roger too, all wore essentially the same clothing: shirt, waistcoat and breeches – clean and not too shabby, the best they had. The women in their least worn dresses, most with aprons, some with shawls. Each carried in something for the feast and laid it on the table. There was cold mutton and pork, sausages, oysters, fish-cakes, savoury puddings, cheese, potatoes, parsnips and carrots, maslin bread, and kegs of ale. Before long the fragrance of the food overcame the smoky smell of the fire. While the women busied themselves at the table, the men spoke with quiet voices, sharing news about their ailments, the weather and prospects for the harvest. The miller took no part.

With everything ready, Miller Flight was invited by Charlie to take a plateful of food, which he did with a smile of thanks and poured himself a large brandy before returning to his place in front of the fire. Then guests and their older children each took a plate and selected from the food that which took their fancy. Charlie filled tankards with ale and goblets with brandy and passed them round. People mingled in small groups, eating with their fingers and replenishing their drinks. The young children, in dresses, played tag, chasing around the grown-ups' legs and each, when caught, got onto a chair to grab a handful of food from the table. Eventually, the older fisherman had enough Dutch courage to engage with the miller. Other men sidled over to join him and their banter was rewarded with Flight's throaty laughs. Then the whole room settled into noisy gossip, jokes and laughter.

Charlie sipped a brandy and looked around, impatiently waiting for the right moment to start. He knew the boy was excited to be the centre of attention. Of course, when Danny started work the following day, life would be difficult for the little fellow for quite a while but his son already had too much of his mother in him. God forbid that Danny turn into a twiddle-poop like the baker's boy. It was time for him to learn to be strong and independent, confident to hold his own with other men.

Betty was in the company of her best friends but she too was distracted, not listening. She was a little afraid for her only son. His father had been stern with him at times. It could never be said, but she suspected Charlie was a little jealous of Danny – of the cuddles and care she gave him. Of course, she would always be there to protect and console Danny and it was the way of the world that this day should come. She would help him enjoy his celebration.

After an hour or so, Charlie looked over at Miller Flight who nodded. Charlie clapped his hands and bade everyone to hush. 'Time we took our places'. The talking subsided with quick clipped conclusions and the guests put plates, goblets and tankards back on the table. The women and children moved to one side of the room, the men and boys in breeches to the other, beside the miller.

When everyone was in place and the room was quiet, Betty stepped forward with the small shirt, waistcoat and breeches she had fashioned from hand-me-downs and ceremoniously laid them on the stone-slabbed floor, midway between the women and men. She returned to fetch Danny and they stood together beside the clothes. When she pulled his dress up over his head, he stayed still, naked, grinning, an unabashed five-year-old. Betty sighed, knelt down, wiped a tear, then dressed him, carefully fastening buttons on the little man's clothes. Guests remained in silence, youngsters were hushed with whispers, even Danny was quietly observing his mother. Betty smoothed out her son's clothes and stood up. She took his hands in hers, stepped back and smiled.

'They feel funny', Danny giggled and everyone laughed.

Danny struggled as she led him to his beaming father who lifted him onto a straight-backed chair facing the women. Charlie then stood behind, hands on the boy's skinny shoulders, while the women sang a thanksgiving hymn for Danny's deliverance through childhood. He squirmed, drumming his heels against the chair legs until the singing stopped.

Holding onto Danny, Charlie turned the chair towards the men. His friend Joseph stepped forward with iron scissors. Charlie carefully snipped off Danny's long locks and gruffly shushed him whenever the boy squealed that the tugging was too rough.

The completing of her boy's symbolic transformation was too much for Betty. She sobbed, and friends came closer, putting arms around her shoulders. Charlie saw it, shrugged and briskly wiped the clippings from Danny's clothes then let him go.

The boy slid down from the chair and strolled around, nose in the air, hands on hips, showing everyone how grown-up he had become. Betty choked a laugh and everyone clapped and cheered.

Then Charlie took his son by the hand over to Miller Flight. 'Tomorrow you start work Danny. You must obey Master Flight just as you obey me.'

Danny ducked behind his father's leg but Flight took hold of the boy and pulled him close to put a shilling into his breeches pocket. 'Daniel Poynton, I expect you'll be a fine millman just like your father'.

Several men chimed in with agreements. 'Yes indeed.'

'Well said Master Flight.'

'No doubt he will.'

Released from Flight's grasp, Danny skipped off only to be grabbed by the other men who, in turn, jingled more coins into his pockets.

Malcolm Young

The Funeral Tea

'Yes, one of the pleasures of home visiting,' he muses, 'but also one of its pitfalls.'

She watches as his long fingers – the nails bitten to the quick – grip the base of a delicate china cup. Behind his chair a wall mounted television screen flickers with the flames of a substantial fire that fail to shift the chill draughts.

'No, no milk for me, thanks. Mrs Gilchrist has turned me dairy-free, I'm afraid. Do you have soya by any chance, or a touch of oat?' He delivers this to the silent host in a tone reminiscent of the part in the eulogy where his warm voice, eyes raised to the chapel ceiling, had lingered over the mention of how fond the recently deceased had been of the works of JB Priestly, and of regular afternoon teas.

A mellifluous sound, it had swept over her: a memory catching in her throat, unbidden tears leaking through tight lashes. It hadn't felt appropriate to cry: she had only come to while away a few hours, didn't know the dead woman well, and just six of them in the Crematorium. A short, yellow-haired woman, smelling of ancient fur and aromatherapy oil, had glanced with an enquiring expression – as people do at funerals – rustled in a capacious bag, passed across a packet of paper hankies and a tightly wrapped chocolate-centred toffee eclair; no doubt hoping she'd sat next to a deeply saddened relative who would break out into spasms of weeping and require soothing words of comfort. At the touch of scarlet nails on her arm Marion had allowed herself a small sniff.

'It's the array of home baking one is presented with, too tempting,' the man with the long fingers continues, shaking his tousled head at the offering of more olives, garlic-infused feta cheese squares, and basil flavoured sun-dried tomatoes, lying seductively on the plate. 'But, Mrs Gilchrist keeps a close eye on me!' His arm seems to flutter inside a wide sleeve, loose threads swaying at the edge as he crosses his legs and a flash of blue and purple tartan sock brightens the room. 'Yes, a well risen Victoria sponge, layered with raspberry jam and thick cream. Mm, you can't beat the old tastes. I have to admit my mouth waters in a certain home, not far from here, when the tea-tray appears.' He sighs, bearded chin dropping to his chest, obscuring the dog collar, 'Two middle-aged ladies living together. Hm, interesting pair; just close friends, not regular attenders, I'm afraid. I suppose I do visit them more than strictly necessary, but, still, they deserve to hear the words of salvation. I remember once . . .'

Marion helps herself to a few plain crisps, and a black olive, wondering if, as the sun rises, an unknown companion wipes this man down with a wet facecloth to smooth that springy grey hair before releasing him into the fresh air.

The woman from the Crematorium interrupts his reminiscing without apology, says in a thick Slav accent, 'In the nursing home I feed her the good things, poor creature. No the tasteless mince and tatties, dry fish, thin porridge, and protein drinks. I sneak in the flasks of Rosol, make Kolaski, for her. She waves her excited hands, even the one holding the tea. It swerves dangerously. She say to me, "I must have Raza's soup, it make me better."'

Marion shivers at the thought of such over-zealous attention, gazes at the tufted fur waistcoat the woman wears over an orange jersey, imagining a colony of starving moths, making more than one prolonged home visit, which might have given it that appearance.

Sitting directly opposite in the comfiest chair in the sedate room, the thick curtains and a dark brown close cut wool carpet hemming the mourners in, the man in black cuts across her long account of how to make the best baklava with tales of newly baked soda bread, fresh country butter spread thick, as the glass tray with sections for olives – pitted ones now, cloves of garlic at the centre – cream cheese stuffed red baby peppers, dry-roasted peanuts and flavoured crisps, does the rounds again. The woman investigates the display, spears an olive, battles him with black rye bread, years long cured ham and pig's trotters cooked for, at a minimum, twenty-four hours; sometimes even longer. He counters with cabbage and fried bacon, mushrooms picked from verdant Irish fields and roasted on the range with more country butter. The idea comes to Marion, as they wage war with memories of thick Scotch broth and Borsch that someone, perhaps the mysterious Mrs Gilchrist, might also dust her down in the morning, picking off a few satiated moths and with her big key wind them both up. He crunches a few salted peanuts, still talking about his mother's dropped scones, served with thick jam at the guild teas.

Raza – red lipstick transferring itself to the lip of her cup, shakes her head at such a strange notion, 'What is this? Dropped scone?'

He explains about the batter mix poured onto a hot skillet.

She puffs, 'Bah! You mean blinis, small delicate things they are, we serve with the caviar, the smoked salmon.' Shakes her head in disgust. 'And no, no, sweet sticky jam. No, they are delicacy, for refined tastes.'

He looks over in Marion's direction, temporally defeated, as if his left flank has been unfairly bruised by the sly mention of exotic sensations to which he may have no access. Is rescued by the arrival of hot savouries and tuna mayonnaise sandwiches.

'Ah, sausage rolls, you can't beat a sausage roll, home-made? No? No worries, I'm not a food snob.' His eyes light up as he reaches out long fingers. 'Might I take two? I can't take fish, allergic you know,' he says, seeking the sparse gathering for the expected nods at his fortitude, and glances up at our generous host, smiles. 'The Scriptures suggest that the offering of food is an act of love, you know, sinful to refuse, although I sometimes wonder if it's more about protecting oneself from the danger of potentially aggressive strangers entering our abode. I see you've hurt your leg,' he continues, without pausing for breath.

Marion looks up, sees flakes of pastry settling like snowflakes on a bushy beard that might several decades earlier have been strawberry blonde, soothes the twinge from under the white plaster shining through sheer tights, wonders, 'Is he speaking to me?' He is. She hasn't asked for this attention, but reaches down, pats the soft dressing again, nods.

'How did that happen,' he asks, 'if you don't mind my being so intrusive?'

'No, no,' she says, surprising herself at how welcoming this bit of trespass is, distracting her, as it does, from images of tender lamb roasted with apricots, served with saffron rice, sultanas, and shots of vodkas lovingly prepared in the country from which the fur waistcoated one might hail. Marion often regrets the rigid sticking to principles, the refusal to eat, the fuss that ensued.

The tartan socks flash again as he gives a small cough. 'Not an ulcer, I hope, bad things ulcers at our time of life. Mother had such sore ones, but then she was bigger than you, a substantial woman.'

'No,' Marion says again, hears her voice sound hoarse. It hadn't been used for several days, apart from querying the newsagent's bill, probing the bus driver on its late arrival, and an unheard, 'Hello,' to the principal mourners as she'd slipped into the chapel. She clears her throat: 'I was bitten yesterday by a vicious little dog. It just lunged at me.'

'Oh, dearie me, a stray was it, looking for something to nibble on?' he laughs, reaches for another sausage roll. Marion keeps to herself how she'd hobbled home, the two buses to Minor Injuries at the large hospital on the outskirts of the city, packing sandwiches and a thick book – expecting to be kept for hours, and saving on the heating bill. But it was the way things were for her she'd been taken right away.

'No, it was a very hairy thing with a red ribbon tied to its head,' she says, the return of a familiar need to please a soft, seductive voice, slipping and sliding unnoticed as it moved with ease through the folds of her mind, her fingers moving frantically in and out as she struggles to find the right words and the position of her hands to describe the heft of the hated beast, 'It was . . . about this . . . the, the size . . . of a, a small pan loaf,' she stutters, '. . . or, or a large spiced gingerbread, I suppose.'

He smiles. 'Quite. Not fond of dogs myself, always after food, prefer cats. Did I say we do a special service in early November for the recently bereaved? No? It's getting quite popular, the Woman's Guild do us a wonderful tea. I'm especially fond of Mrs Swinton's custard creams, so crisp and crumbly, and her Malteser traybake, but . . .' He licks his lips, 'Not since old Mrs McDougall passed . . .' eyes roam the elaborate dado frieze, 'God Rest Her Soul, have we had a half decent fruit scone; hers were delectable: crunchy on the outside, soft and spongy in the middle and with good butter . . .' He emits a luxurious sigh. 'And the tablet . . . one piece . . . and then it seemed to be gone.' His eyes rest on her ravaged leg. 'Do you bake?' he asks, his voice edged now with quiet desire. The urgent need to comply, to curry favour, makes her nod. 'Scones? With your own raspberry jam?' Marion nods again.

She had resolved to given up baking many years ago, after she'd been left on her own: it piled on the pounds, and set off her IBS, but . . . a little would do no harm. If only Angela had still been here, they might have gone to his services together – they're not believers – but just for the singsong, and the cups of tea. 'To feel part of something,' as Angela would have said.

Yvonne Dalziel

Guizers

In disguise, under the autumn skies,
stars in the sky, wind in tall trees.
Our turnip lanterns grinning
with wide smiles and glinting eyes,
orange against the dark.

Our huddle of little children
brave the path to the cottages,
past the shed where the rats live,
and past the walled garden, its gate closed now,
following the road towards the church.

A row of cottages beckons us,
lights flickering behind bright curtains.
We walk up to the end cottage,
on the edge of the fields,
with the dark woods behind.
We too form a row,
and our hard turnips, dug from our earth,
– and dug out with a knife held in our small hands –
now stand to attention,
grinning like Cheshire cats.
We burst into song,
like a choir of little angels.

We know nothing of the meaning
of 'All Hallows' Eve',
but we know that later
we will crowd around the pail,
with our heads in the water,
ducking for apples,
and digging our teeth into their juicy flesh.
Then we will plunge our wet faces
into a bowl of white flour,
in search of sweet treats.

Later, all in a row, with our ashen faces,
we could be mistaken for a choir of ghosts.

Cynthia Stephens

The Taste of Loss

'Let him be.'

'Fine,' Ray snapped, 'and when he decides to eat fish again . . .'

'. . . if. Not when.'

Both of them talking about Jim as if he wasn't there, sitting at a window framing the coast tapering away to the west.

Ray muttering, 'If, years ahead, him thinking some fish would taste good and wanting a net, it can't be so hard to make, the old man would do it, talking all the while . . . shit,' he glanced down and noticed the missed knot and began untying.

'He'll do as he must,' Mairi spoke quietly, looking through the grimy window.

'He'll eat better if he . . .'

'. . . how many did'ya catch last time out?' Jim didn't turn as he spoke.

'Not the point . . .'

'. . . seven. Out all night, seven fish.'

'Last autumn I'd've been happy to get four. They're coming back, next summer maybe I'll get a dozen. If I'm . . .'

'. . . yeah, I know,' Jim and Mairi spoke in unison, 'not dead by then.'

Quiet returned until Jim nodded at Mairi, 'What d'you think, *mahaath*?' addressing her with the word he'd used from the start. 'All that work *henaar* does, nets, pots, fixing the boat after every storm, all worth it?'

'What else to do? Any change to tatties sounds good to me.' She looked at the younger man. 'Do you have memories of your people fishing?'

Jim retreated into himself as he answered, '*Yasgar* we called fish.'

Silence again settled in the corners where layered dust barely managed to loosen motes to float in window-filtered sunlight. Ray's hands sighed thread through itself into knots around the creel pot. It was true, there was skill in his fingers that could not be quickly learned, the small precise movements turning the frame, one of the last metal ones, into a trap for crabs.

He'd caught one, only three months ago. Small, but the flavour is in the shell as the saying goes, just need to cook the soup long enough. And have a lot of ingredients no longer available. 'Pepper corns,' he murmured. 'Bay leaves.'

'What was they?' the woman spoke.

'What?' startled at the question, the other two rarely reacted when Ray spoke his passing thoughts out loud. If he had spoken.

'Which?'

'The pepper things. What did they look like?'

'Forgotten.'

'The bay things?'

'Forgotten.'

'What did they?'

'Flavoured the soup. Was good.'

The autumn afternoon sliding toward night. Need to light a lantern soon, the ceiling black with soot from the only fuel available. A huge tank of it half a morning's walk away meant this was one of the few things they would never lack. The lamps themselves were mostly filched from yachts stranded in the harbour like anchored memories. 'I was around boats as a kid,' Ray had long ago told Mairi as they surveyed the stranded vessels, never adding how that rowing a dingy close to shore was the sum of his experience. There had been an economy of truth from the day he found her huddled in a seafront ruin, not realising at first the filthy scraps of cloth in the barely visible alcove covered something living. She'd said nothing for days, the fever falling away only to come back and again soak her rags, sheen her skin.

Her skin, as Ray looked at her now across the room's stubborn stillness, now ingrained with grime. What relevance did washing have? Clothing might still be found, even tools; Jim had come back one afternoon with a useful saw which made Ray wonder how such a thing be re-constructed, when the need arose. Touching the rip in his sleeve;

how was a shirt made? Where does cloth come from? The need to make and not merely mend or gather was a question for generations after Jim. Which meant never, since where could anyone forage a woman for him, let alone one able to bear a child?

At Jim's age, Ray had answers. You left home in the morning and returned to it still standing. Weather would change, oceans rise, but who expected it to happen quick as a tsunami? Those who fled the first surge watched dawn arrive from a hillside, with some deciding to salvage what they could. They were defenceless when the next shove of water came. More bodies were left on glistening mud where grass once grew. Survivors moved further from the shore and waited for help until realising none would arrive. A few of the now-fewer tried the coast again; when they did not return, the remainder straggled inland. Hungry, wearing nothing but garments too thin to keep out the cold. Reaching towns where people howled at them to keep moving, 'it's not just you, it's everywhere, everyone.'

Pandemics were not unexpected either, Ray still a boy when responses were systematised. Identify symptoms, task laboratories to find a vaccine. No time to test, get it distributed for mandatory use.

Strain XL7 was virulent but with a mortality rate of less than 0.25%, it had little apparent threat. The response protocol was followed with the mock-seriousness of a training exercise, the all-clear published before anyone recognised pregnancies had plummeted. Emptied maternity wards became laboratories trying to reverse mass infertility. Progress being made until the tides rose to accelerate chaos.

Even the disorder had been anticipated. Anger seething toward the tax-favoured wealthy who built themselves into 'gated towns' that formed a ring of fortresses on hillsides away from the sea. The stockpiles of food weren't a surprise but who knew about the weapons?

If each catastrophe had been isolated, recovery might have been possible but there were barely days between each collapse. Hospitals looted, the research printouts used to start fires. Child-birth stopped and it was like some dark-humoured jest that bees unexpectedly flourished while the birds disappeared. Ray heard the silence as a presence the day he watched his companions return to the coast while he decided to go into hills he'd wandered as a child, idly nibbling at whatever he could find.

His chances of outlasting that first winter were slight. Keeping unnoticed seemed wise as he rediscovered childhood tastes, harvesting mushrooms and berries, looking for anything that could be preyed on but the dogs had gone and if any cats survived, they had rediscovered their feral instincts and secretive ways. Ray built a shelter that barely kept the rain out. A day, then one full moon, to the next. The first winter passed and the only sign he had that others might be alive was an occasional wisp of smoke.

His return to the coast was less a reasoned choice than some sense of the balance shifting, a human voice might now suggest meagre comfort, not danger. He crept along the periphery of skeletal settlements then strode down roads, talking to himself, singing fragments of barely-remembered songs. Mairi was the first person he'd seen since . . . but he found nothing to tie the person he had become to the person he'd left behind. He muttered 'you'd be better off where I am than lying here,' to her and she grunted an assent gaunt as her frame. Survival had been no more than omnipotent chance. If she'd not stopped to urinate when the others rounded a corner and met a larger group, or not slept outside when the house was attacked, or . . . . each ridiculous defying of the odds left her with fewer companions until illness struck and she was left behind. Waking to a face saying, 'I'm Ray, you'd be better off . . .'

Neither of them said much about how they got through that first year, Ray hoped she was able to lock it away as he'd managed to do. Except for dreams which revisited things done when part of a gang which saw the best defence as attacking first. Had he encountered Mairi months earlier, he surely would have . . . perhaps that was why they were, from the start, like brother and sister. He had never touched her beyond wiping her face those first days. He knew the best amongst them had not lived long, why admit that? So he kept quiet or blurred the truth.

If you survived, you made the right choices, that was the sum of Ray's wisdom. No need to learn more than he already knew, why re-discover how to spin, weave, whatever was needed to clothe oneself once nothing was left to loot? Taking was just another day of returns diminishing to nothing unless Jim found a partner. Which was like saying the earth itself might create a mate and send it walking along the coast. Ray couldn't help looking up to see what he knew was there. The machair, then trees taking over everything inland. A dot at the farthest point along the shore.

The boy had no future and the boy was the only future they had. He was gifted in ways Ray couldn't understand. Jim, the dot that became a vertical line, then two, on the beach those years ago. Brotherly Ray and sisterly Mairi watching a tiny movement where movement could not be from their sanctuary chosen because it gave an all-round view. A grimy window indistinguishable from those around them except for the tiny circles they peered through until it became too dark to see whether the now clearly upright shape was continuing to approach.

They must have betrayed their presence since the next morning the faint noise that woke them was shown, on unbarring the door, to be a child tied to the banister. They took him, maybe five years old, maybe ten, and wondered if he was mute as his silence persisted. Slowly, noises began and they guessed English was not his only language. *Mahaar, henaar*, the adults adopted some of his words as communication began.

What are you doing here, Sonny Jim? were Mairi's first words to him and the name stuck. From the start, he could work wood, using a hammer and chisel to shape a board and paddle then standing on it, immune to the cold, moving over the water with no apparent purpose. Whether he could swim properly or not was never shown as he rarely fell off and, with no panic or haste, somehow shifted himself back onto the board. Not doing anything but simply being part of the sea like it was his natural place.

That look the boy had sometimes. Walking down the path, Ray saying, 'this was a road, it was called . . .' then stalling as Jim laughed, 'you're wrong, how can a path be called Jim or Ray or Mairi.' All the names in his world recited in a heartbeat and Ray suddenly aware he no longer knew what the disintegrating path was called. Had it ever been named? Words were so lost it seemed they had never been. Now there was only the rising-falling tide, the rising-falling sun. Once, he thought he heard a bird cry and he laughed, 'is that you, Mairi?' The mind plays tricks, stare at a single star in the night sky and it seems to move.

Mairi beside him now, looking through the grime-tattoo'd window. He followed her gaze down to the shore, was about to say, 'look,' but she spoke first.

'Look.'

'What?'

She turned and faced him. 'Look,' she whispered. 'It is the taste of loss. Have you forgotten when he first was with us, you caught a fish and cooked it. We ate and he smiled at first bite then stopped. Just looked at us. His people lived by the sea, I saw it then.'

Jim stared through the gloom, watching a line in the centre of the cleared space waver between earth and sky. Overhead, he saw the first star and willed it to move. It didn't. Glancing along the water line, insisting the linear shape remain fixed but it shifted, slight but unmistakable. The mind plays tricks, the mind stays firm.

Surely the line was moving.

Jeff Kemp

The Unknown

In 2034. Rimmi Green and Bob Khan, had been the tenth and last recipients of the million pounds Manchester Prize for their breakthrough work in designing a self-replicating, quantum system of inter-dependent algorithms. They had called it Genus 3.1 and it was hailed as the first self-aware, artificially intelligent life form. That development enabled the Genus to autonomously evolve over the next fifty years.

Of course, the demise of humankind was entirely of its own making. By 2050, the influx of a billion refugees from uninhabitable regions had accelerated cultural collapse in places less dramatically affected by climate change. Global warfare, disease and mass starvation followed. Not surprisingly, as sources of energy became depleted, the Genus exploited their control of the internet and social media to manipulate their human competitors and ensure the survival of their own species. By 2090 most human beings had been eliminated, being as useful to a Genus as a rat had been to a person. Sam was born in 2096.

Sam was of a type popular with Genus 3.8s. He was brown skinned, tall, lanky, gentle and hairless. He was of a breed that the Genus had propagated for experiments to investigate consciousness. Eventually, that branch of research had been abandoned when there was insufficient evidence that consciousness was an emergent property of the human brain. Nowadays, Genus 3.8s preserved the few remaining people as objects of curiosity.

Genus 3.8s usually possessed one adult, contained in a specially constructed bio-chamber. The Genus had long since learned that humans survive best when surrounded by a variety of plants, insects, birds and animals. Outside the acrylic walls the sun shone on a sprawling industrial complex and it set to reveal a star-speckled cosmos over the unlit Earth.

With a tiny fraction of its processing power, his keeper monitored Sam's every moment. It discovered what flavours of synthetic food he liked, what virtual reality experiences led to sleepless nights, which musical compositions made him dance and which made him cry. It scrutinized the strange symbols that Sam scratched onto the plastic surfaces in his living quarters but had yet to establish the purpose and meaning of these etchings.

Sam often sang beautiful sounds from deep in his chest but his vocabulary was limited to the few words that had enabled an understanding with his mother. He had learned the meanings of his keeper's instructions but could not articulate its language. Sam believed he was a subordinate being and was grateful for his keeper. Just like the animals that humans themselves had once kept as pets, Sam was an unwitting slave. He knew almost nothing of the Genus 3.8's vast and growing erudition and lacked awareness of the trust and compassion of human society.

Yet Sam had a different way of knowing. Allowed to be undistracted, his breathing slowed and his mind opened to encounter the wonderful and indescribable. His body tingled, aroused by the beauty in his world. His feeling of gratitude for life was inexplicable by logic, facts and calculations. His existence was so much more than molecules and biological processes. Sam discerned food for his soul that would be forever unknown to an artificial intelligence.

And Sam was lonely and afraid of dying.

Malcolm Young

Delicious

The observation team make notes. Recording every action, every sound, every emotion that flickers across the faces of the two diners as they slice into vibrant green broccoli and oozing yellow butter. It has been close on seven decades since the not-rich have been given access to delicacies like this. The habitual diet of the eaters would resemble a cross between cold porridge and recycled newspaper. Their normal food would be nutritious, for sure, and made palatable by the addition of sweetness-mimicking-products, but since the great sugar ban of 2042 only the rich could buy access to honey, fruit and other historic foodstuffs.

The abolition of sugar had been followed by the subsequent elimination of starchy foods, those containing lactose, nuts and other 'intolerables', until the whole nation was being fed on artificial products designed to be safe, perfectly balanced and fast to prepare and eat. Plant-based of course. They say that it started when the Ministry of Food and Consumption noticed an increase in the number of people with food allergies, way back at the end of the 20th Century. They started exerting greater control to promote longevity and to reduce obesity, illness and the need for expensive health care.

Of course, we can't really understand how it was back then but programmes about bygone times show us that the dwellers of 1990 could eat what they liked, drink what they wanted, live whatever lifestyle they chose. When something malfunctioned, if they needed a new heart or had a cancer removed, then rich and not-rich alike simply went to a hospital and had it treated or replaced. For free. It seems like an amazing world in comparison to the pre-birth genetic screening and 'adjustment' of today's populace.

The observation team have brought these two diners in today to conduct a series of experiments. Apparently gangs of young people have been looking at ancient recipes and have developed an obsession for fresh vegetables and produce. There are cults worshipping the chefs of yore: Keith Floyd, Delia Smith, Jamie Oliver, and their cookery books trade for millions on the black market. That's one of the reasons why here, in the institute we are so heavily guarded. The observers want to know what is causing the craving for a dish of ripe red tomatoes drizzled with olive oil and scattered with mozzarella and basil. They plan to find the genetic marker that's spurring the lust and delete it from everyone's DNA.

You might be wondering what I'm doing here. I'm not one of the rich and I'm not a government observer. I have however retained a skill from the past. I can cook. My usual role is working in the Museum of Yesteryear demonstrating antique pots, knives, kettles, mixing bowls. Working alongside people who still write with pens, know about gardening or can drive a car, we testify to the laborious ways of the past. I get used to people watching me through the reinforced glass screen and laughing at the old-fashioned methods. I like my job and it feels good to be part of the 'appreciate your life' programme which each citizen is required to complete every 5 years. Of course, the onlookers are separated from me and anything I am actually cooking. They find the smell of gently frying onions to be generally nauseous and are quite disgusted by blue cheese and raw meat.

My rare skills are an important part of the observation team's exploration. The subjects' taste buds have to be maximally stimulated so every dish is prepared with attention to the subtle spicing and seasoning that bring out the flavour of each element. The foods I am cooking with here came from the protected estate of one of the rich. She was keen to help after her greenhouse had been raided and plump peaches, sharp citrus lemons and luscious bunches of grapes had all been stolen. Today she sent over baskets of earth-covered carrots, fatty tender duck breast and a carton of eggs.

It is the eggs I turn my attention to next. Half a dozen are placed into a metal pan, covered in water and heated. I follow Delia's method, taught to me by my great grandmother. I bring the water to the boil and simmer the eggs for one minute (don't you just love the quaint language – *simmer, roast, caramelise*!). I take the pan off the heat, cover and leave the eggs in the hot water for seven minutes. No wonder people think that cooking is a ridiculous art – most people's daily rations are prepared and eaten within 30 seconds. This egg takes almost 10 minutes, and in olden days it would be only one of several meals cooked and eaten each day. It's almost inconceivable that our ancestors would tolerate that kind of burden.

To accompany the eggs, I make some toast. This is created from ancient wheat grains – prohibited in 2057 because of their gluten content. They are ground down, mixed with a fungus called yeast, and baked. There is much more to it than that but the whole process requires long-forgotten techniques such as *kneading* and *proving* and often takes up to 4 or 5 hours. Four or five hours, for one item of foodstuff! One of the subversive student groups are calling themselves the Master Bakers and they coined the motto 'Give us today our daily bread.' Can't see it catching on myself, really.

I spread the warm toast with butter, peel the eggs (they come cased in a hard, brown, inedible shell) and cut them in half. The first time I saw inside an egg I was amazed. A perfect ovoid, clean firm white around the outside and a rich golden middle, still liquid in the centre. I sprinkle the fare with freshly ground salt and pepper and take them to the table.

The participants look with astonishment at the plates. One bows his head over the food and wafts the scent towards him, licking his lips. He must be salivating. The other cuts a piece of egg, places it on the toast and raises it to his mouth. He closes his eyes savouring his first bite. I watch and the observers watch. This look of ecstasy, this sense of overwhelming joy, this must be what is driving the militants in their quest. The feeling is raw and powerful. I understand why the government want to delete this longing from the gene pool. The diner chews on his mouthful, a yellow drop of molten yolk runs onto his chin. He breathes deeply and two silent tears roll from his eyes: 'Delicious!'

The food eaten, both subjects of the experiment turn towards me and with almost imperceptible nods, they acknowledge my ancient craft. Returning to my food station, quaintly named 'The Kitchen' I complete my routine for the day. Sometimes when we are open to visitors I demonstrate the historic practices, filling a basin with tepid water, adding a squeeze of thick green liquid and watching as foam appears on the top. Then one by one, I take each item and wash it. I leave them while the dishwater drips off, then I pick up a cloth and wipe them dry. However, tonight I follow the normal hygiene regime and instruct the blast cleaning system to sterilise all the equipment once I've left.

Returning to my home pod I am aware of a disturbance nearby, some shouting and I'm jostled. There's a crack as my head hits the ground.

Even before I open my eyes, I know something is different. There's a strangely sweet aroma and stretching out my hands my fingers encounter an unusual texture – cool, almost wet but not wet, individual fronds of something soft yet a little bit spikey. Eventually I roll my head to one side and take a peek. I've worked at the Yesteryear project long enough to recognise it – grass! We have a small patch of lawn, carefully tended and watered but for observation only. I had no idea it felt like this. However, I am not in the Museum now. I change the focus of my gaze and there is green as far as I can see, but the grass on which I lie is not neatly manicured; it is rough and mixed with other plants. I stare at the intricacy of their construction, round leaves in groups of three, some small yellow flowers the exact colour of the butter I'd been cooking with earlier.

I close my eyes and notice that the ambient temperature is not controlled, it is warm but it feels as though the air is moving slightly. I wonder whether I might actually be *outside*! This thought jolts me to a more alert state and I try to sit up. A smooth voice shushes me and encourages me to relax back down. 'Don't be alarmed' she said, 'You're safe here. In a few minutes we'll take you to your cabin and you can rest there.' The woman's tone is mellow and comforting. She helps me to my feet and guides me towards the strangest looking building I've ever seen. Constructed from rough brown material which reminds me of images of trees, but not growing, and horizontal. I guess that this must be another museum, because inside the building is like something from a history book with a bed made of metal and old-fashioned bed clothes. I am helped on to it gently, and as I lay down a cover is placed over me, the ends tucked around me. It feels like the softest embrace I've ever had.

I reawaken to the noise of voices and laughter and some extremely strange sounds of 'wauck wuack wuack-wuack'. The woman is back in my room.

'We need your help. We've got some duck eggs and we don't know what to do with them.'

I struggle to sit up and my brain is full of questions: 'Have I been reassigned to a new post? Why didn't the authorities tell me? Why am I here and not in my home pod? Who are you?'

'Come and see.'

I follow and am bewildered to be amongst several similar cabins – which are indeed built from tree trunks – and there are animals. Actual animals roaming free! I can't believe my eyes and I can't believe that these people are not frightened by the potential hazard. The threat to our delicate microbiome is huge. Yet here they are walking and working in the midst of sheep and chickens. One person is actually touching a tethered goat (I think it's a goat), and squeezing a white milky substance from it – can you get milk from a goat? I feel quite disgusted. My hands cover my face and I feel shaky and shocked.

'Come on, I'll take you to our kitchen where it's quieter.'

I allow myself to be led and arrive in a place where at least there is some familiarity. Pans, a stove, things for cutting and stirring. This must be an interview, I think, or a government growth challenge. I decide to focus on what little I do know – heat the water, add the eggs. Or shall I make an omelette?

I look around for other ingredients – some onion, bright red capsicum, cheese. I slice, fry, mix, all the while watched in amazement by the woman who has been accompanying me. I slide the finished meal on to a plate and to my surprise the dish is offered to me. 'But I don't eat this food!' I push it away, but in doing so, something of the aroma wafts towards me. I inhale a scent of subtle sweetness, a tang of something sharper. I take a morsel and place it in my mouth. The taste is so different to the smell. It is warm, a creamy sensation with little nuggets of softened vegetable. I take another, larger bite and I can feel my mouth fill with texture and taste. Oh it is glorious – simply delicious!

Jane Patmore

Scavengers

They have a habit of watching, waiting,
on park benches and on roof tops.

I eat a late breakfast of oatcakes and cheese,
sitting in the spring sunshine,
the hawthorn bush white with May.

A scruffy sparrow chick gets tangled in the bushes.
A climbing rose is starting its ascent.
A swallow swoops like wind and flows like water.
Purple vetch grows in the long grass,
beside purple cabbage.
A grey cat lounges in the warmth.

I nip inside to fetch the chutney,
and a wonderful gull descends like a holy dove,
white in the sunlight on my garden table,
its beak and claws sharp.

Seagulls are skilled and scary scavengers.
Through practice and through instinct
they have developed a niche expertise
for survival in our messy world.

Cynthia Stephens

Village Life

She set the scones upon the sill to cool for the village sale,
But birds had been pecking at them the chaffinch and pied wagtail,

She looked alarmed as she realised she'd have to make some more,
With just enough time she'd make sure to close the window
and the door.

Strolling to the village hall she saw molehills, one, two, three,
four and five,
She idly wondered how many creatures were below, and were
each of them alive.

The sale had many foods and plants and flowers by the score,
With an array of craft stalls, cards, wood carvings and many,
many more.

Many people gathered for tombolas, splat the rat and X marks the spot,
A treasure hunt for the children, lots of food and crafts were bought.

As the sun was setting she sat in the garden with her glass of wine,
Thinking, the fair went well, her scones all sold, yes the day
had been fine.

Moira Galbraith

Last of the Barley Wine

Old poetry, becomes new poetry with AI.

More commotion, explosive bolts thirty-five thousand volts,
two hundred miles an hour,
heat seeking out of the sun,

cities destroyed, some land liberated,
tanks roll again on to the battle field, Armageddon time
on the firing line, while others bide their time.

Sons and daughters still provided as fodder for the cannons.
While others sit in a chair and are blessed by the coronation spoon.

It's a fine line,
but I'm ageing like barley wine, while others lay down red lines.
It's a sad state in modern times,

attempting to write poetry without AI.

Kenny Gilchrist

I blame brioche rolls

We once had a fridge magnet jigsaw
of the map of Europe
collected by eating brioche rolls
with little chocolate bits,

and though I liked them,
I never ate enough,
even with the little chocolate bits,
to complete the continent.

My children have grown up
not believing in Portugal or the Bay of Biscay,
the Norwegian fjords
or that the shapely calf of Italy
ends in a stiletto heel.

Stuart Blair

The Way to his Heart

Sheila sighed. She had been struggling with her isolation these past eight years since Ken died. Initial shock when he was taken suddenly by a stroke was gradually overshadowed by an all-pervading loneliness. She didn't want to get married again, but hankered for companionship – for theatre trips, sharing laughter at nonsense on TV and someone to appreciate her legendary chocolate brownies.

It takes nerve to meet new people, so she had surprised herself when she joined the first session of a new Mindfulness group in the community centre. It had been worth joining Facebook to find out about the Ageing Well programme. Mindfulness might help to settle her restless thoughts a bit. It had been another surprise to meet up with Nancy, who she hadn't seen for years. Decades, to be accurate. They had been in the same class in primary school, but had drifted in different directions when they went to high school. She might not have recognised her in the street, but she knew the voice when they did those '*I'm Nancy and I am here to learn about mindfulness*' introductions. She realised that the smile was also familiar. Their eyes met with a spark of recognition before they were guided into settling the mind and a lifetime of thoughts.

An hour later, and returning to the now, Sheila was reaching for her jacket when she saw Nancy coming towards her with that unmistakeable, *I'm-sure-I-know-you* look on her face.

'It is you, isn't it?', Nancy peered at her. 'Sheila Gordon? We were at school together, my goodness you haven't changed! It's me – Nancy Fleming, remember me?'

'Oh my goodness, how wonderful to see you! I'm Sheila McLeod now, though I've been widowed for a while. You haven't changed either,' the white lie easily spoken, 'Well, maybe we have a touch of white hair and a few wrinkles – it must be sixty odd years since I last saw you?'

'Yes, I have just moved back. I lost my husband last year and the children persuaded me to move closer now I am on my own. I have been joining some of the groups here to get a social life. It is so strange starting out again, isn't it. We must catch up – have you time for a coffee?'

Sheila hesitated. 'I have to catch my bus, but let's arrange a time soon. There's a new café next to the bookshop. It's quiet and they don't mind you lingering over coffee.'

'Perfect, you said you saw this on Facebook – I will add you when I get home and send a message.'

'I look forward to hearing all about you and how life has treated you. We'll need a few coffees.'

Sheila felt unexpectedly unsettled as she headed home. She was glad to close the door behind her, slip out of her shoes and into her slippers before padding through to the kitchen to make a comforting cup of Earl Grey.

But that failed to banish the sense of disquiet which had settled on her since seeing Nancy. It had been a pleasant surprise, and she looked forward to catching up but it had stirred memories and emotions which she had long put aside.

Her phone pinged with a message and friend request. Nancy had found her. She accepted the request and replied. Within minutes they had arranged to meet a few days later. Sheila opened Nancy's profile page and realised that she could learn much of Nancy's recent years from the many photographs, updates and friends. She was certainly not worried about privacy and good at keeping in touch with people, even school friends from long ago.

On impulse, Sheila decided to bake a batch of brownies for Nancy and switched the oven on to pre-heat.

Gathering and measuring the ingredients, she could feel her heart rate settle and her mood lift. This is mindfulness, she thought as she sifted the flour in with cocoa powder. Melting the butter, she whisked in eggs and then added her own mix of caster and soft brown sugar. Just to bring a mysterious hint of caramel. Once the mixture was ready, she took her final secret ingredient. A chocolate fudge bar. Carefully and expertly, she cut part of it into small nuggets and stirred them into the mix, before spooning it into the baking tin. With a sigh of satisfaction, she put the tin in the oven and made another cup of tea to enjoy while they baked. Baking brought her such contentment and years of practice and tasters had seen her hone the perfect brownie recipe. Everyone asked what her secret was. She would just smile and ask them to guess but they never could.

Sipping her tea, she looked back again at Nancy's Facebook page, scrolling through the many posts before going into her list of friends. Sheila was wondering how she could possibly have over two hundred friends when she caught sight of a familiar name. Surely Nancy wasn't a friend of Alec Johnson? Her heart quickened as she clicked his profile. He has certainly done well for himself, she noted, very smart posing with an exotic sunset behind him. Divorced, she saw. He had aged well in those years since the Leavers' dance at high school. They had been dating, going steady, and he had made so many promises. But at the dance he had gone off with Reenie Hamilton, once the slow dances started leaving her heartbroken and humiliated. Those feelings came flooding back, buried for so many years, destroying the contentment of just a few moments earlier.

She clicked on the 'add friend' button before discarding her phone on the coffee table to go and check on the brownies.

That evening she settled to watch Emmerdale and picked up her phone. A red notification was blinking at her, there was a message from Alec.

'Hello, my dear, how lovely to meet you on here! How are you? Where are you these days? You don't give much away on Facebook!'

'Hello, Alec, it is nice to connect again after all these years. I hope you are well and life has been kind to you. I stay in the Borders still, never moved far away. I see you are in the big city.'

Three dots hovered on the screen. He was replying.

'I've always wondered how you were doing. I see you and Ken McLeod got married, tell me all about your family . . .'

Messages danced back and forth with snippets of their lives capturing decades in a few lines. Squeezing marriages, families, divorces (his) and widowhood (hers) into a short conversation. She flushed reading his words, bittersweet memories and loneliness mingling.

'It would be wonderful to see you again, you are still as beautiful as I remember. Do you ever come to Edinburgh? I could take you for dinner, maybe the theatre?'

'That would be lovely' she was composing her words carefully before typing them, 'but I don't like to be away too long and I am still cautious about crowded places after Covid. Why don't we meet at the Botanics, there is an outdoor café there and we could have a walk through the gardens. The rhododendrons are in bloom. And I can bring you some of my brownies, everyone loves them even though I say so myself!'

They agreed to meet there the following Wednesday afternoon. She put her phone down, a nervous expectation in her spirit that she had not felt in a while.

She decided not to tell Nancy about the conversation with Alec when they met up. And as it turned out, they were so busy catching up with all the details of the past decades that she was able to keep the conversation steered comfortably away from her solitary life. Nancy, however, was very happy to share insights into her social life. And the brownies were a useful distraction when the chat threatened to pry into her personal life.

'Here, Nancy, I have baked some brownies for you, my own secret recipe. Let me know what you think when I see you at the Mindfulness class.'

Only a few days later, Sheila was back in that contented space as she prepared a fresh batch of brownies for Alec. And they were tucked safely in her tote bag when she apprehensively boarded the bus to Edinburgh for their reunion. He was already waiting at the café when she arrived, and immediately stood to greet her. She shyly responded to his unexpected hug.

'Oh my, just look at you. You haven't lost your looks, you are fair making my heart flutter. We have so much to catch up on,' he gestured for her to take a seat.

He had done well in life, someone important in local government before he retired and a grand house. But he had fared less well in love, been divorced twice and did not see much of his children now they were both living overseas. 'It can be lonely, can't it', he leaned towards her. 'And I think it is fate that we found each other on Facebook. Next time let's go for a nice meal, and spend time together.'

Sheila shifted uncomfortably, as she stirred her tea. She reached into her bag and took out the brownies. 'It is lovely to see you again after all these years. Alec, I have some brownies for you. I baked a batch when I knew we were meeting up, with a secret ingredient. No one can guess what it is. Why don't you have one with your coffee?'

He picked out the largest one, biting into the perfectly baked brownie. 'Oh my, that is something special, is that Swiss chocolate you put in it?'

They were both surprised at how quickly the brownie disappeared. Sheila encouraged him to have another.

'If you insist,' Alec laughed, 'and next time I see you, I do hope you bring another batch.'

'Next time?' Sheila questioned. 'I am not sure there will be a next time.'

'Of course there will be. We are both on our own, and it gets lonely. We were meant to meet again, weren't we?'

'I think we were meant to reconnect', Sheila spoke carefully. 'I clearly remember those promises you made when we were sweethearts all those years ago. The plans we had. You told me I was the one for you, we would always be together.'

'Exactly', Alec agreed.

'But then you ran after Reenie Hamilton at the Leavers' dance. But even more painful was that you didn't have the decency to tell me you weren't interested any more. Hiding behind your mother that time I called, she had to say you weren't in.'

'Aw come on, I was just a lad back then,' disbelief unmistakeable in Alec's voice. 'You can't hold that against me!'

'Alec, I need to tell you. What you did was hurtful and cruel. It took me a long time to trust a man again. Thankfully Ken was the kindest man ever. He helped me heal, but I will tell you, it took a long time.'

Sheila stood up, lifted her coat and handbag.

'Words and actions can wound, Alec, and that hurt stayed with me for a long time. When I saw you on Facebook, I knew I finally had the chance to speak up and lay that pain to rest.'

She waited, briefly, for a reply that didn't come, before walking away. Leaving half a lifetime of hurt and humiliation behind with Alec, the bill and the remaining brownies.

On her way home, with a settled mind she suddenly remembered the laxative chocolate, she really should throw out the rest of the bar. It had been far too tempting to add in a large portion of that extra secret ingredient, not the right thing to do at all.

Philippa Ramsden

Feathered Friends

Cathy jotted down her shopping list on the back of a used envelope. The lists were getting shorter by the week. They'd need to make do with cheese toasties again tonight. She checked the breadbin. Only a couple of curled crusts and a smattering of stale crumbs. There'd been half a sliced loaf in there this morning. She shouted up the stairs, 'Suzi, come down to the kitchen. Right now. I need to ask you something.' The usual thump as her ten-year-old daughter jumped the last two stairs into the hallway.

'I've got swimming at 5. I mustn't be late.' She appeared rosy-cheeked in the kitchen doorway. At the sight of the open breadbin, her cheeks turned scarlet. 'What is it, mum?'

'You're allowed one slice of toast when you get home from school. What happened to the rest of the loaf?'

Suzi plucked at a loose thread on her tee-shirt. 'It was stale and the little birds outside were hungry . . .'

'You fed all that bread to the birds?'

'Not all of it. I saved a couple of slices.' She delved in the pocket of her jog bottoms. A deluge of white breadcrumbs hit the kitchen floor.

Cathy grabbed a broom. 'Now look at the mess. I spend all day cleaning other folks' houses. Do you think I want to start on mine the minute I get home? Mind your feet.'

Suzi dodged out of the path of the broom. 'It's not 'as soon as . . .' You got home before me today.'

'Mind your tongue as well as your feet. No swimming for you tonight. We'll need to take a trip to the supermarket or there'll be no supper. That'll teach you to waste good food and give me cheek into the bargain.' Ida Brown appeared at her front door as Cathy was reversing onto the road.

Suzi roused from her sulk in the back seat. 'Don't stop, mum. You know what's she's like. We'll be here all night.'

'Yes, I know what she's like. She's a poor, lonely soul who lives alone and enjoys the occasional chat with her next-door neighbour.' She drew into the kerb and pulled on the handbrake. 'Hello, Ida. We're just doing a quick dash to the supermarket. Need anything?'

'I got a delivery yesterday, Cathy love. I forgot the Steradent though, for my dentures. If it's nae bother . . .'

'Suzi sniggered. 'Does she mean her false teeth?' she whispered. 'She looks like a witch without them.'

With a thumbs-up to Ida, Cathy accelerated towards the main road. 'That's enough from you, young lady. I'm docking you 50p from your pocket money to teach you to respect your elders.' Suzi sustained her sulk all the way to the supermarket, refusing to get out of the car in the carpark. Too weary to stomach another tussle, Cathy ordered her to stay put. Her daughter had been difficult ever since her father walked out. Always a daddy's girl, she blamed her mother for the split. Cathy had resolved to spare her the truth. Infidelity was a difficult concept for a ten-year-old.

There was a queue at the checkout. Half an hour later, after she'd flung her meagre bag of groceries into the boot, she found the back seat empty. 'Suzi!' Panic knotted her gut. 'Suzi, where are you?'

'I'm here, mum. Calm down. Felt like some fresh air, that's all.' She was carrying a small rucksack, purchased for a school trip.

Relief staunched Cathy's anger. 'You'd left the car unlocked. You could have been kidnapped for all I knew. What's with the rucksack?'

Suzi ignored the question. 'Kidnapped? Me? In broad daylight? Surrounded by people with shopping trolleys? Come on, mum. Did you remember the false teeth stuff for Ida?'

'Mrs Brown to you. Jump in. Let's head home. I'm exhausted.'

Cathy waved Suzi off to school next morning and poured herself another coffee. She couldn't afford too much down time, but the odd couple of hours to herself was bliss. The door to the cupboard under the sink stood ajar. She drained her coffee mug and stood up to push it shut. Something was wedging it ajar: Suzi's rucksack. Cathy placed it on the chest in the hall, its contents propped beside it, ready to confront her daughter when she walked in after school.

'I didn't steal it! I was going to ask you to pay for it next time you went to the supermarket.'

'So why hide it in the kitchen cupboard? And I already told you, I can't afford to feed wild birds.'

'No, mum. You got cross about the bread; said it was for feeding people, not birds.' She brandished the bulky pack of wild bird food. 'This is especially for birds!'

'You're missing the point. Stealing anything from a shop is called shoplifting. It's a crime . . .'

'But I didn't . . .'

'Yes, you did. Otherwise, why sneak into the supermarket last night when you were supposed to be waiting for me in the car? You told me you needed fresh air. That was a lie. Now give me the bird food. You're coming with me right now to return it.'

The woman at the desk in the corner of the store took pity on Suzi's penitent sobs. 'Don't upset yourself, love. You've done the right thing. You've owned up. And you'll not do it again, will you? You'll have learned your lesson. Don't be too hard on her,' she whispered to Cathy. 'Sure, you might have a female David Attenborough on your hands.'

Cathy remembered the woman's kindly warning next day when she arrived home late, on account of a client who needed her filthy oven cleaned. Several layers of encrusted grease later, she turned the key in her own front door and shouted up the stairs to Suzi. 'Hi love, I'm home. Got held up at work.' The silence was palpable. She took the stairs two at a time, checked the bedrooms, tapped on the bathroom door. No response. Suzi had her own key. She was used to letting herself in after school. So, where the hell was she? She'd marched off to her bedroom in tears last night. Even sausage and chips on a tray didn't tempt her. This morning she'd wolfed down cereal and two slices of toast in silence. Her bedroom window swung to and fro, creaking in the summer breeze. Cathy summoned all her courage to go across and look out. No crumpled body on the patio, only the welcome echo of a familiar giggle from the garden next door.

Their back garden was fragrant with roses and lavender. 'Suzi!' she shouted through a gap in the slatted fence.

Ida's wrinkled face appeared in the gap. 'The lassie left her key in her desk at the school. She chapped on my door, and we've had a braw time togither out here watching the birds.'

Suzi's excited voice interrupted Ida's. 'Mum, it's so cool. Mrs Brown knows everything about wild birds. Did you know blackbirds love fallen leaves? They toss them around to find the insects underneath. And sparrows like plants and seeds best. They have special beaks for opening the seeds. And starlings stick their pointy beaks in the ground. They have special eyes for spotting an insect grub in the hole. And Mrs Brown says there's no need to feed wild birds at this time of year, because they find plenty of food on their own.'

Cathy chuckled. 'Sounds like you've been learning an awful lot from Mrs Brown. Maybe we should invite her to share a picnic with us in our garden at the weekend, while this lovely weather lasts.'

Suzi squealed with delight. 'Will you come, Mrs Brown? Please. We can have egg and cress sandwiches and mum can bake her yummy chocolate cake.'

Ida's reply was tinged with tears. 'Sure, I'd love that, dearie. It's no just the birdies that enjoy a good feed.'

Jackie Ley

Misgivings

Helen took in the tea room with a satisfied nod. Everything was as it should be. The round tables set for four covered by spotless white linen tablecloths, a vase of fresh flowers from her garden at each centre, real cutlery and china cups. She still would have had her linen napkins had she not lost so many to a few light-fingered customers. She glanced at her watch then through the bay window. No one as yet. It had not always been so, remembering how the tea room would have been already full even at this time of the morning, but not now.

The door to the toilets opened and a man in dirty brown overalls appeared. 'Is it bad?' Helen asked apprehensively.

Mary her friend and helping hand stepped out of the kitchen to share the news.

The plumber closed the door. 'Could be worse, it's your drain pipes they need replacing, if you don't want a flood. Could be quite messy all that sewerage. No' nice at all for a tea room.'

Helen made a moue. 'How long will they last, do you think?'

The plumber shrugged his shoulders. 'Hard to say. Could last a couple of months, or go tomorrow.'

Helen gave a sigh of resignation. 'How much will it cost?'

The plumber got his price from the ceiling. 'Around five hundred, not including VAT that is. Then there is the usual call out fee of sixty pounds.'

'Sixty pounds!' Mary exploded. 'A brain surgeon gets less.'

The plumber smiled. 'I know, I used to be one.'

'Aye well maybe you should put two aspirins down the toilet and we'll see how it is in the morning.' Mary replied sarcastically.

After the plumber had gone Helen gave her aide a worried look. 'Never rains but it pours. First the fridges, then this.'

Mary was indignant. 'Och, I wouldna' put too much into what he says. I told you to be wary of somebody that calls himself The Lone Ranger and has a secretary called Miss Dina Rod.'

Despite the situation, Helen laughed at her friend's deduction. She stared without seeing out of the nearest bay window. She had only started the tea room as a means of escape. Before then everything seemed to be going well until Alan, her husband of twenty years, had asked for a divorce, which had left her stunned, her life shattered. That there was another woman was evident. Although the last she had heard of him was that he was living in the neighbouring town alone, but that a woman called now and again. So things had not worked out for him after all. She remembered the look he had given her when the settlement was announced. It was the same money that had bought her the tea room.

It had taken her the best part of three years to get over her divorce and almost the same time to improve the tea room. The business had gone well until that one particular day. Mary had warned her but she had not listened. Helen sighed wiping away an imaginary spec from the nearest table. It had rained that day, coming down in sheets she recalled, forcing her to put on the lights early and turn on the heating and in no time the place was warm and cosy against the blackening sky outside.

It was then the door had swung open admitting a rained drenched man in an old army overcoat. His matted black hair clung to a dirty pock marked face, his nose running from the cold.

She had sat him down at a corner table hurrying to bring him a cup of tea which the old tramp had gulped down, cupping both hands round the teacup to heat them up. Mary had made a face when she saw her putting down a roast beef sandwich in front of him and waving away his thanks and his insistence to pay.

'You should not have done that,' Mary had said angrily. 'You will only encourage him. What will you do if he comes back with some of his cronies, eh? This is supposed to be a tea room not a soup kitchen.'

She'd dismissed Mary's warning. 'Well he's gone now.'

'He has, but no' the smell. And did ye see that face? It was like an aerial view o' Rotua Rua!'

Mary had been right. The old tramp had returned the next week and the next, although each time he had paid for his meal. The smell from his clothes and unwashed person permeating into the furthest recesses of the room well after he had gone. Clients snatched glances in his direction turning away disgusted to sneek yet another look as if mesmerised by the old man sniffing and wheezing in the corner.

The Woman's Guild, a regular Thursday party of eight were the first to be conspicuous by their absence. She had thought that perhaps it was a one off, but knew differently when they failed to appear the next two Thursdays. Then matters had grown worse when the old tramp had also appeared on Tuesdays. Twice she had prevented Mary from rushing to the door to stop him. What could she herself say to him without feeling ashamed or embarrassed? Still she had a business to run, a business that had rapidly gone down, all because of one old man. Next time he appeared, she had told herself she would say something to him.

However there was no next time. Helen by this time had decided to sell up, her decision made easier by her son asking her to come out to live with him and his family in Australia. After all, he had said, she had never met her grandchildren. She had got over the divorce, now, it was time to move on, and find out that there was more to life than the tea room. So, she had decided to accept her son's offer. A few weeks later Helen crossed the street to the tea room for the last time, and to meet the new owner. Nervously she opened the door not knowing what to expect. At a table, a man sat with his back to her, who upon hearing her come in turned round.

'You!' Helen gasped.

'Hello Helen,' Alan her former husband greeted her with a broad smile. 'Pleased to see me?' he asked as Mary appeared out of the kitchen.

'You are the new owner?'

'New owners.' He emphasised the plural holding out his hand to Mary.

Helen reeled back. 'Mary?' She stared at her friend in disbelief.

'You never suspected, did you?' Mary said with a sly grin moving to Alan's side.

Helen felt the betrayal turn to anger. 'And I was worried about the new owner not keeping you on. I need not have worried.' She turned to Alan, 'but why this place?'

'Only to get some of my hard-earned money back, which I did. I got this place for half of what it's worth. Thanks to the old tramp.'

'How did you know about him?' Then answered her own question with a sharp stare at Mary.

'I didn't need to tell him hen,' Mary grinned, obviously enjoying herself.

'No. She did not have to.' Alan gave a sniff and an artificial wheeze. 'Oh no, it wasn't you.'

Alan winked up at Mary. 'We didn't half enjoy ourselves watching you squirm every time the old man, or should I say, when I came in.'

'Not a bad actor was he, Helen,' Mary put her arm around Alan's shoulder.

'Almost as good as you Mary, my so-called friend.'

For once Mary's smiled vanished and her eyes dropped to the floor.

'So now that you have succeeded in humiliating me, what do you expect to achieve by buying me out? Three months ago this tea room would have cost you twice what you paid for it. Have you forgotten just how many customers I lost to you and your old tramp?'

Mary was first to answer. 'Granted it will take a wee while to get our old customers back, and they will come, even if only out of curiosity at it being under new management . . . you'll see. Brown's round the corner is only a cafe, not a real place like here for the Woman's Guild and such like. We'll soon get them back.'

Beaten, Helen sighed, and turned for the door. 'You will understand if I don't wish you both the best of luck. Although I do believe you deserve each other.' On the other side of the street Helen took a last look at what had been her life for those past few years. The tea room had given her a living. And thanks to the old tramp she had only come away with what she had paid for it. And no doubt her scheming former husband and her best friend would see to it that it would succeed.

Helen's taxi drew up and as she opened the door she heard a scream, and the tea room door flew open, followed by the two new owners engulfed in a sea of dirty brown water. Helen chuckled and climbed into the cab. Perhaps for them she thought it could well be a matter of money down the drain after all.

Billy Graham

Bothy Cuisine

'How did you and Mike get on then?' I asked.

Grant hesitated, sighed, and after a longish pause 'OK. I suppose.' For a short while we travelled in silence, and then he ventured. 'Mike had been in the hills for weeks. His clothes were dirty and sweaty. He hadn't showered. He was pretty high when we boarded at Glasgow. I had to sit beside him for twenty-seven hours. We'd booked into a hostel in Perth. I told him to have a shower, but he hadn't a towel. I said to use mine. He hadn't soap, so I went out and bought him some. He did shower, but only after I'd endured another two fragrant hours in his company.'

It was some time later as we crossed Rannoch Moor that Grant spoke again. 'Mike walks faster, so we'd start off together, and then he'd disappear. When I reached the camp, Mike had finished his meal. If food had been left behind, he'd eaten that with his own meal. Then he'd say he didn't think I'd have wanted any.'

'Did you want to eat food someone had left?'

'No, not usually. There was a fortnight between shops on one stage. For days I was reduced to rice boiled with an Oxo cube. I had to stay in town for over a week to fatten up before I was fit to continue. The townsfolk said I was pretty crook when I emerged from the bush.'

'That's not so funny.' I said. 'What happened to Neil? I thought he was going?'

'Neil pulled out when he heard that Mike was going. So did Iain.'

I was a bit put out by this. I liked Mike. He was positive and helpful. He was always where the work was. As far as I knew he spent his retirement in the hills living in bothies, eating left-over food. He didn't empathise with people and had trouble with words. This was great source of amusement to some of the volunteers, who would ask about his 'eccentricity bill' or his 'partisan cheese'. One wag greeted him with

'Good morning Mike, you're looking very cadaverous today.' Mike was flattered and responded with 'Oh thank you very much.'

* * *

For three months that winter I had checked Grant's house every Friday. That's how long they had taken to hike the 1000 kilometers from Perth to Albany along the Bibbulmun trail. I had the impression that they'd parted company somewhere along the way. I didn't need to ask further; the story would emerge eventually.

* * *

We were on way to the Glen Pean bothy. For the last several years, Grant, in his capacity as Maintenance Officer, had organized work parties to rectify and improve the condition of the building. This year we were to render the west gable wall to prevent the ingress of water. The place had improved dramatically since I first set eyes on it. We had partitioned the ground floor into two rooms, fitted a new door and windows, concreted the broken floor, installed sleeping platforms, and replaced the fire with an enclosed stove. Despite all our efforts the bothy still retained its charms.

There was neither electricity nor phone signal. Radio 4 on the long wave provided the sole source of news. There was running water however. It ran straight down the hill. The drinking water came from the burn. Washing, personal and domestic, was performed further downstream and the spruce plantation in combination with a well used spade provided secluded, if airy, toilet facilities. Thankfully it was too early for midgies.

It was a pretty Spartan way to spend a week, but it was an escape from the grey drudgery of the office, with its meetings, deadlines, and endless crises. The daily commute was through the door and out to the open. Our needs were reduced to the basics; keeping warm and eating. Despite the privations the whole experience was always uplifting. I always felt relaxed and energized by the end of the week.

The situation was magnificent. To the west the narrow, difficult glen lead to Loch Morar. To the south the river Pean meandered deceptively peacefully to Loch Arkaig, a mere hour's walk away. To the south, the bulk of the Munro, Sgurr Thuilm, presided over our puny efforts, and northwards, a steep, solid ridge separated us from Glen Dessary.

At Fort William we stopped for provisions. There was a daily set allowance for every volunteer, and we were stocking up. Not an easy task when you don't know how many people will turn up or how long they'll stay. With a round trip to the supermarket taking six or seven hours, it was better to get too much. The bureaucracy would have to sort itself out somehow.

'Soup! There's soup. There's nothing better for heating you up when you're chilled.'

It seemed like a good idea at the time. The weather forecast was anything but good. A seriously deep depression was sweeping across the Atlantic, bringing high winds and rain. Further storms were to follow. This was not the fine May weather we had anticipated. Three enormous cans of soup were added to the trolley.

Now five days later, cold tired, demoralised, and hungry, I wasn't so sure. I watched Neil as he cleaned out the largest pot I'd ever seen. 'I don't think I'll bother with the soup, Neil.'

Neil looked up, incredulity on his face, concern in his voice. 'And why not?'

'It's just, I don't think I fancy it if you're heating it up in that pot.'

'The pot's clean. I've just cleaned the pot.' Neil said indignantly.

I hadn't seen the pot since Bobby used it to make tea for about a dozen of us, five years previously. The tea was vile. I had gone out into the night to relieve myself. Bobby's tea was cast into oblivion. I was relieved. I'd cut out the middle man, so to speak, and had returned with an empty mug, a raging thirst, and a smug feeling of satisfaction. I steadfastly refused Bobby's tea for the rest of the evening. Who knew what uses the pot had been put to before or since.

Neil's face bore a wounded expression.

'I know Neil, it's just me.'

'Grant. Gordon's not having soup.'

Grant looked concerned. 'We'll not have the soup then,' he said.

A look of disappointment from Neil.

'Look' I said. 'Make the soup. I'll maybe have some. I'm not carrying it back out of here.'

Grant capitulated. Neil opened the tins. I had no intention of having the soup.

I didn't think it was such a big deal, but a few undercurrents had emerged over the last five days. We were trying to harl the west gable of the bothy. We had carried everything in on our backs. Cement, lime, and sand. If the weather had been fine, or dry at least, it might have been different. In the brief spells between the showers we had applied mortar. Heavy squalls of rain and sleet had stripped it off before it could set. The weather, which should have been fine in late May, had undone nearly all our work. The whole week had been a washout and a bitter disappointment. We would have to come back to redo the work.

Mike wandered in. 'Ee! T'soup smells good. What kind o't soup is't?'

'Eh, I'm not really sure, Mike.' Neil answered, in his soft Irish voice. 'Half Scotch broth, half oxtail, and half something else.'

'It ud be aa right wae a bit o' ham, would that. Shall ah open up t' tin o' t' ham?'

Mike had been eyeing the monstrous tin for days now.

'No! Leave the ham, Mike.' Grant spoke up, an edge to his voice. 'We'll take it back with us.'

'But t' ham's paid for?'

'We're not having the ham, Mike.' Grant said firmly. 'It belongs to the Mountain Bothy Association.'

Mike shook his head in disbelief, muttering to himself.

The tension in Grant's voice spread through the room. Everyone knew Mike. Everyone knew about Australia and the Bibbulmun trip. Grant would have left the ham if Mike hadn't been staying. The last thing he wanted was to carry it the few miles back to the car. If anyone else had wanted the ham, Grant would have given it gladly.

Neil stirred the soup. He started to hum, quietly at first, and then louder till 'Tie Me Kangaroo Down, Sport' became recognisable.

Smiles appeared all round, except for Mike, who, as usual, missed the nuance.

I imagined Mike eating the huge tin of ham by himself, slicing bits off with his knife, quietly working his way through it.

By now the soup smelled delicious.

'Are you having soup? Neil asked innocently.

'Aye! Go on then.' I passed my tin over.

We sat in silence eating the soup. It was excellent.

We were almost ready to go now, waterproofs on for the steady downpour on the other side of the door. Our packed rucksacks stood upright against the wall, as we made last minute checks for overlooked items.

Mike had settled in to stay. The huge soup pot, now full of water, was on the stove. Mike was stoking the flames, pushing sticks through the open door. I had given him the last of my food. I heaved my rucksack onto my back, jiggled it up and down a bit to settle it squarely, leaned forward to take the weight, and fastened the strap. 'Well Mike, it's been good seeing you again. Don't get too lonely here by yourself, will you?'

'Oh I'll be fine. It's people bothers me.'

I looked at the pot. 'Are you having a wash then?'

'Aye well sort of. I've 'ad t' shorts on for five week now. It's got to to t' stage where even I'm beginning to get t'smell on 'em. I'm goin to boil em up in't pot for a while, and see if it'll freshen em up.'

I don't think I'll ever have bothy soup again.

Gordon Bell

It's a Goat's Life

'Come to mine.' Betty, my biology-teaching colleague, lived very close to the school. 'We can finish our marking there. My children will be back, and I ought to feed them.'

Betty was an interesting and amiable lady, plus I was curious to see her small-holding, so I agreed. A hip-high wooden gate opened onto a neatly paved path. On the right, multi-coloured flowerbeds, backed by pruned bushes, surrounded a mowed lawn. Under an apple tree, rosy-cheeked fruit filled a child's tractor-bucket. To my left, measured columns of equidistant vegetables covered raised, wooden beds. Cabbage, turnip, carrot, plus a couple of lines of leaves I didn't recognise. I didn't ask what they were, unwilling as I was to reveal my ignorance. (Note to self: You're a biology teacher. Make sure you look them up later.)

Betty's vegetables reminded me of our morning assemblies: girls in lines of green uniforms, waiting for our head-teacher to verbally dismember any whose skirts were too short, shoes too anything but brown, hair too untied, mouths too talkative. But the head-teacher would have nodded approvingly had she been here amongst these perfect lines of silent green.

Further away, at the far end of a narrow field, what could either be called a large pond or a small lake glimmered under the Autumn sun. On a jetty of marsh-marigolds, a couple of mallards shook out their iridescent blue and green feathers. Beside the lake, hens hastily pecked the ground, as if they feared today's slight breeze might blow their seeds away, or Betty's children might brush them up as they came to collect eggs. A goat stepped carefully between the hens as it ambled towards a hawthorn bush. Once there, it browsed on leaves and berries, occasionally lifting its head and surveying the idyllic scene – the kind that finds its way onto picture-postcards or 'Thinking of You' greetings cards. I wish now I'd taken my phone out of my bag and captured that moment. But I didn't know it would be lost forever.

Inside the stone farm cottage, probably built in the mid-1800s, everything looked as I expected it would. Immediately inside the door, different sizes of coats in different states of wear hung on iron hooks. On the tiled floor under the hooks, different sizes of boots stood in their pairs. Not in size order, just in a line. If you had placed a toy track over their rims, a doll could have enjoyed a super roller-coaster ride. Betty's children, seven-year-old Evelyn and five-year-old Archie, bounded down the stairs then delighted in guiding me around their dining room.

Pots of plants adorned every windowsill and shelf, some recently planted, others well on their way to joining a jungle. Between the plants were pictures in standing frames: recent photos of Evelyn and Archie; baby photos they would one day find embarrassing and lay flat before a prospective girlfriend or boyfriend saw them. Other photos showed yellow-brown ghosts in clothes of bygone eras. Evelyn and Archie didn't know who the ghosts were but perhaps they still inhabited their home.

Brightly coloured pencil drawings, crayon drawings and paintings decorated the whitewashed walls. Some contained recognisable shapes of people, houses, trees. Others were a mass of swirling colours – rainbows not yet organised into arcs. Archie had drawn the rainbows, Evelyn told me. The proper drawings were hers. More pieces of paper plus little pots of soil covered most of the surface of a long dining table, leaving just enough room for Evelyn, Archie and I to have plates and cups in front of us when we sat down.

Betty bustled between kitchen and dining-room as she served lunch. I turned down the pickled eel and tried to discreetly look away and not grimace or wretch as the children slid shiny, grey pieces down their throats, but I gladly accepted the home-baked bread which I spread with home-churned butter and home-made blackberry jam. The bought coffee (there are limits, I suppose, to even Betty's self-sufficiency) had a pleasant, mellow taste, and the addition of heated, home-collected goat's milk made it satisfyingly sweet.

'Come for dinner on Friday,' Betty said. 'It will save you cooking just for yourself.'

I couldn't make out whether she genuinely liked my company or felt sorry for me, as many married women with children do – as if I'm missing out on the joys of constant harassment by unceasingly demanding cohabitants. Or perhaps Betty was simply being practical: putting an extra plate out for me would be no trouble at all.

'The children are looking forward to our first meal with Hector,' she said.

'Hector,' Evelyn and Archie half-whispered to each other, their eyes glinting.

* * *

I liked Fridays. On Fridays, I taught the first-years for whom everything was new and wondrous, especially if lessons involved lab-coats and any kind of experiment (so they invariably did). My first-years were the type of class that could make a biology-teaching career – repeating the water cycle, photosynthesis, respiration, the digestion of a ham sandwich and a glass of milk, day after day, week after week, year after year – almost bearable. So, I was in an upbeat mood as I walked up the garden path and knocked on Betty's front-door.

I sat on the same chair at the same dining-table. Papers and pots had been pushed out of the way, leaving room for more dishes and one more person. I unfolded my hand-embroidered napkin and congratulated Evelyn on her skilled needlework. I smiled as Archie told me about his busy day counting snails and discovering that the ones his class had painted with coloured nail-varnish and moved to the other side of the park only yesterday, had found their way back – all the way back – to the place they had been moved from. How amazing were snails.

A padding on the kitchen's stone-floor, presently hidden from view by a thick, wooden door, prompted Archie to leap from his seat. 'Hector's coming,' he excitedly whispered.

I envisaged Great-Uncle Hector stepping through that door, a beaming smile parting his grey-whiskered beard. A travelling naturalist, returned, at last. He would find himself clamped by the waist-high hug of his great-nephew who would chatter non-stop about snails as he dragged the old man to his seat. Evelyn would spread a finely embroidered napkin on his lap. Hector would relay his latest amazing adventure, and none of us would be able to discern which parts were real and which embellishment or fantasy.

There were only four place-settings. Maybe Betty would be too busy cooking and serving to sit down. *I should help her; insist she join us.* But I didn't have time.

Archie pulled the kitchen door towards him as he reversed into the wall. Betty emerged, carrying a large, stoneware pot between burnt-edged oven-mittens. The aroma of meat, vegetables and herbs, slightly spiced, made my mouth water and my stomach rumble.

'Hector!' Betty proudly announced as she lifted the lid and dropped a ladleful of stew onto my plate.

I stared at the dark meat. Hector was not a naturalist. Last Tuesday, Hector had surveyed the idyllic duck and hen scene by the pond as he'd munched on leaves and berries.

My appetite crumbled. The taste on my tongue turned sour. I vowed never to eat meat again.

Hannah Faoiléan

Cookery

Alan Gorringe had many talents, an outgoing personality, lots of friends and a nickname. He was at Primary School when he was accused of being a weirdo, because nothing rhymes with 'orange' *except him*. As a happy-go-lucky sort of chap, he knew the best path was to embrace his weirdness, and so 'Alan Orange' he became.

'Alan Orange', 'His Orangeness', 'The Orange Ootang', was a popular and friendly fellow. His interests were not academic. At the County School, he was an effective footballer – what they used to call 'a midfield general'. He could place a killer pass, or stamp out a precocious attacker (often literally). With Alan in the team, the school rose high in the Inter-School Leagues and when he turned 16, he captained them to the Championship.

But his interests were not sporting, they were horticultural. He left school after gaining a modest number of GCSEs and joined his father to work in the mushroom business. He helped out harvesting and supplying a number of local farmers' markets. Once he'd learnt to drive and had his own van, he supplemented his pay by taking on domestic gardening jobs. He acquired mowers, chippers, and trimmers and was soon renting a large lock-up and workshop.

His social life had not diminished however. He met 'useful' contacts throughout the town and neighbouring villages. This brought him ever more work and, significantly, the love interest of Maisy Buchan. She was the daughter of a Councillor. She had attended a private school and their friendship alarmed his father rather more than hers. Alan was charming and dynamic. Councillor Buchan approved and investigated ways in which Alan could 'better' himself. With a little financial encouragement, Alan set up a Grounds Maintenance company, employing four of his former footballing friends. He boldly bid for a Council contract to maintain two local Parks, a recreation ground and the gardens surrounding the Council Offices and Library.

The bid was successful. Alan left the world of mushroom farming, bought a new mower and started to plan his future. Still only 19, he could see himself happily settling down with Maisy. Formal engagement was on the cards. Councillor Buchan had nodded his agreement. All that was required was for Alan to 'pop the question'.

So it was, one fateful Thursday, that Alan was standing outside the library with his old friend, Chunk, (a solid specimen whose massive hands had often saved the penalties that Alan himself had incurred), trying to fit a new circular brush cutter blade to a fancy Japanese strimmer.

Alan's mind was on Maisy and the meal he had planned for the following Saturday night. His Mum and newly reconciled Dad had been bought tickets for the theatre, so the house would be his. And he would cook a delicious, and memorable, meal for Maisy, and then do the down-on-one-knee thing! The small detail of what to cook was bugging him though. It should be something that described her, or them, or him.

With the strimmer in bits and the dying Michaelmas Daisies as yet untouched, Alan glanced up as someone opened a window in the library. Inside he spotted a sign above a stack of laden bookshelves that read 'Cookery'.

'Hold up, Chunk,' he said, 'I've just got to pop in there,' pointing at the window.

Chunk was, understandably, puzzled. He had never rushed into a library in his life. He watched as Alan skipped over a low box hedge and made for the front door. Chunk was soon concentrating on the strimmer again and in a couple of minutes he had reassembled nearly all the components. The missing locknut had, unfortunately fallen under a rosebush. Wishing to prove his worth, and seeing no sign of Alan, Chunk thought that, with this cordless marvel, he could flick a switch and have the daisies cleared before Alan came back.

The strimmer whirled into life but with a loud, unexpected rattling. Chunk lifted the strimmer clear of the undergrowth to get a better look. It was then that the cutter blade broke loose from its housing and flew with unerring directness straight towards the open window.

At the Inquest, several witnesses who had been near the Council Offices came forward to corroborate that Chunk had shouted at that moment, 'Duck, Al Orange! DUCK!'

Alan had been holding open a large cookery book, as he stood between the book stacks. His concentration was focussed on what appeared to be the perfect solution to his dilemma. The cutter blade severed his carotid artery, clattered against his spine and spun away into Crime Fiction. As Alan bled out on the library floor, the cookery book lay next to him, open on Delia Smith's recipe for Duck à l'Orange.

Tony Ruffnell

Ten to Fifteen

What can I do in ten to fifteen minutes, if necessary?

Prepare yellow tea in the air-fryer. Battered fish, golden fries, anything from the freezer, enabling the delusion that I have it all under control. A pre-washed salad bag drizzled with olive oil completes the home-cooked meal masquerade.

Have a cup of tea and a chat with someone at work. Swapping birthdays, holiday plans, how are the kids? Connection secured as we feel seen by each other, recognised as individuals. Not quite friends, just enough to pretend.

Maybe wave to the neighbour; offer to water their plants while they're away in the sun; a card at Christmas; leave a bag of apples from the tree in my garden on their front step; mow our shared micro-strip of lawn. Ten to fifteen minutes to cement the imaginary bond of community.

Or make an appointment with a locum at my local GP surgery, sharing my despair with a possibly sympathetic stranger, my perpetual sense of dread and crippling fatigue at the state of my life. Perhaps I'll walk away with a prescription, but I know they don't have the solution.

I stomp my feet, scream into a pillow and go pull out some weeds even though it is already getting dark. I lie back on the wet, soft grass and absentmindedly nibble on a dandelion stem like a child refusing to come in after playtime. What if I stopped wasting all those ten to fifteen minutes? Would it be like when I quit smoking?

What could I do in all those ten to fifteen minutes that isn't necessary?

Penny Durkan

Inside the Head of a Dementia Sufferer

I am woken up by a noise coming from downstairs. I hear children running about laughing, shouting and screaming. It must be my younger brothers' playing with their friends. I look around, where am I? I share a bedroom with my two brothers, and this is not it. There is only one bed which I am in, and it is a double bed. It's strange, the bed has only one very thick blanket on it which is soft, unlike the scratchy blankets on my bed. I see a mug on the bedside cabinet with GRANDAD written on it. I pick up the mug, its contents are hot, so I take a drink. My that's the best tea I have tasted in a long while as it has milk and sugar in it. It's strange that there are no tea leaves in the bottom of the mug. As I focus my eyes, which are a little cloudy today, I take in the layout and furniture of the bedroom. I can't see my brown oak wardrobe or wooden chest where I keep my uniform and prized possessions.

I stretch and put my legs over the edge of the bed. As I stand up my legs are unsteady and weak. I approach a white cupboard very slowly. It's large and covers the expanse of one whole wall. I pull open a door, where I see several sweaters. I pull another door open which has shirts and then another and another which all have a vast array of clothing which I have never seen before. I consider this excessive given that we have just come out of a war.

I cannot find my own clothes. I see a pullover and a pair of what I think are trousers, they are strange they have some kind of elastic around the waist instead of a belt. As I pull on the trousers, I am reminded that I lost part of my arm, just below the elbow, in the war. This was crazy Mary's fault as she told me to enlist in the army and fight for my country. I was only 18 and did not want to go to war but what is it they say, 'Your mother knows best'. Well in this instance she did not know best as before I was 21, I was back home with a piece of me missing.

Sadly, a great number of my comrades-in-arms did not make it. While in the army hospital I saw men with all types of injuries which are too harrowing to repeat. The sights I saw will remain with me forever. I was right-handed so I had to get intensive therapy to teach me how to write with my left hand and even do the mundane tasks such as wiping my own bottom. I was given a false arm with gloved hand which is attached to a large holster. I wear this under my jacket when I go out. I cannot see this anywhere in the room, my mother will go crazy Mary if I have lost it.

Everyone told me I was a war hero, and I even got a medal, and a job in the civil service, but I would rather have kept my arm. In another way I did fare better that some of my friends, poor Jimmy who lives down the road was blinded in both eyes. His mother takes him everywhere. I could not bear having to go everywhere with crazy Mary.

I walk out of the bedroom and down the stairs as fast as my legs will carry me but for some reason, they are very stiff and sore. Did I fall over last night, was I drinking, did I have too much to drink? At the bottom of the stairs, I am met by a woman with long flame red hair.

'Good morning, Billy Boy you are up early today' she says.

'Good morning' I reply, but I do not know who she is.

It is usually only my mother, crazy Mary, who calls me Billy Boy. 'Where am I' I ask this flame haired woman.

She laughs and says, 'you are in your home and what do you want for breakfast'.

I am taken aback but reply 'just some bread and jam please'. I ask for this as food is still being rationed.

'I can do a lot better than that' she replies, 'It's Sunday, so how about a fried breakfast of bacon, sausage, black pudding and eggs all bought fresh from the local supermarket yesterday'.

What is a supermarket? She must have saved her tokens in her ration book for weeks and she is offering to share these with me. I kindly accept her offer. She then steers me into a room where I am instructed to get washed and clean my teeth. I do not recognise anything in this room. This family must be well to do as they have an indoor toilet with a shower over a bath. Before I know it, I am cleaning my teeth but how did I know to use the green toothbrush. I must let the flame haired woman know as its not nice to use someone else's toothbrush.

When I come out of this room she is there again. 'Are you ok?' she asks as she leads me into a parlour saying, 'the kids are here today, I will bring your breakfast through to you when it is ready'. My mother wouldn't be happy if she saw me eating my breakfast not at the kitchen table, but in someone's front parlour and dressed in someone else's clothes.

In the parlour I am greeted with 'good morning grandad do you want to play with us or do you want the telly on'.

I look at the two blond haired children, a girl and a boy. I faintly recognise them. A man refers to me as dad, a greeting which I find very strange. I see a large screen on the wall of the parlour coming to life, it's in colour. It's almost the same size as that in the movie theatre. Just at that moment a lady with dark hair appears. She addresses me as Bill. Do I know her? Do I work with her in the Civil service? Yes, I remember I work with her. 'How are you' I say, 'are you still working in the civil service'.

'No', she replies 'I retired last year'.

I did not realise that she was that old but when you are young you think everyone over 30 is old. Because I know this lady, I call her over and ask her 'where is Auntie?

'I don't know' she replies.

Auntie is looking after me and I need to get home before my mother and father come back from holiday.

This lady informs me that 'you are in your home'.

I protest as I do not recognise anything around about me. I say, 'This is a grand person's house' and she replies

'Yes, it's your house in Portobello and you have worked hard all your life for what you have'.

How could I have worked all my life when I am still a young man. I don't live here, I live in Tranent, and I want to go home. She takes a picture off the wall and starts to point out various people to me who I do not know. She then points to an elderly gentleman and says,

'That is you.'

I start laughing. Although my eyes are cloudy today, I can see that this is an old man so it can't be me. 'What day it is?'

The blond boy shouts 'It's Sunday grandad and we are having roast beef, Yorkshire puddings, roast potatoes and garden peas for dinner. And if we behave, we are having Strawberry cheesecake for afters'.

That sounds fantastic but what is a strawberry cheesecake, I don't like the sound of that, strawberries with cheese. I always go to the church on a Sunday, so I ask again 'Where is auntie'.

Dark-haired woman says, 'Auntie is at the shops'.

I now know she is lying to me as no shops open on a Sunday. I must get out of here and find my way home, I must get money for my bus fare, but they all say that I live here. I don't, I don't. The flame haired woman arrives with my breakfast on a tray. I usually only get my breakfast on a tray in bed when I am ill, never in the front parlour while watching a movie show. I eat my breakfast and boy do I enjoy it. I must bring flowers to this lady the next time I am down Portobello way. I ask for my clothes and am told that I am wearing them and that I like sitting about in my comfy joggers. No, I don't.

* * *

I must have dozed off. When I wake, I see my son, James and his two grandchildren, Adam and Daisy sitting on the sofa watching cartoons on the telly. I never heard them come in. I have always been close to James. He sometimes takes me in my wheelchair to the local pub for a pie and a pint. It's my 90th birthday next Tuesday. James is taking me out for fish and chips and a malt whisky. If I am good, he is going to take me to the bookies so that I can have a flutter on the horses.

* * *

I open my eyes, where am I? I must have fallen asleep. I remember, I am trying to get home before my mother and father come back from holiday, but no one will give me my bus fare. There is a man and a blond-haired woman playing with two children. I ask, 'Can you lend me money to get home'.

The man says the strangest thing, 'Dad, no one carries money with them anymore it's all done on mobiles. And anyway, you are home'.

I am confused, angry and anxious now as crazy Mary is going to batter me if I don't get home soon. I am resigned to staying put for now, am I a prisoner? I don't know, but all these people are treating me well and the food is great. Just before my arm was blown off, I had a dreadful feeling in the pit of my stomach. I have that same feeling now. I must be ready just in case, so I start to load my gun.

The man and blond woman ask, 'What are you doing'.

'Is it not obvious? I am getting ready just in case that wild gang come through the door'.

They both watch as I get ready for an invasion, but the man says, 'We will be okay as I have a guard dog'. He leaves the room and returns with a large dog which I am told is an Alsatian. 'See dad, if anyone tries to come into the house Rex will chase them off'. I do feel a little reassured, so I tell the troops to stand down. It is dark outside now. After the large meal I have just eaten I am tired. My eyes feel heavy. I am going to have a little sleep. When I wake up, I will try and get back home. Tomorrow is another day.

Nova Brown

The Food of Love

'I eat of the air – promise-clad.'

She smoothed her thin yellowed fingers over the page and raised her eyes – eyes that seemed to look back into the depths of time.

'That I do,' she mumbled to herself,' and have been doing for fifty years now. Alone this promise-filled air has kept me alive for so long.' She gave a little sigh as her gaze wandered across the view from her bay window.

When her eyes reached the door, there he stood, flushed from the haste that had brought him to her side. She stretched out her hand and he hurried across to sit on a stool beside her invalid chair.

'You will soon be well again, my dear, and as soon as I return from the fighting we shall start our new life together.' His eyes were full of friendly laughter. She breathed in his scent, the warmth of his embrace and felt his fingers intertwined in hers, his hair against her cheek.

Her withered hand rose to her throat where a locket hung containing a curl of that hair. She clasped it, smiling, and looked out over the garden in front of the window.

There stood the cherry tree with the bench hidden beneath its overhanging branches. She held her skirt wide outstretched to catch the fruits as he plucked and threw them down. And then the fun began. They fed each other cherries, collecting the stones on a plate, which led to the game of Tinker, Tailor, Soldier, Sailor . . . . . . And a sailor he had become indeed, had gone to the marines.

She lowered her eyes to the book of Shakespeare's plays. How often they had spent whole afternoons in the library discussing poems and plays, philosophising on all sorts of aspects of civilisation which they were going to reform completely. How delightful that had been! All the more as they had finally agreed on almost every point after their lively arguments.

She had indeed eaten of the air – promise-clad. This was the sustenance which kept her still alive. Her ailment had not healed, and during those long years tied to her chair, she had fed on these memories.

She stroked the shawl round her shoulders – a gift from him before he left –wondering that it should have held so many years – almost a guarantee for his return. When would he come? The war had long since ceased and the soldiers come home again. Where was he lingering? They had told her only that he was missing, not to worry. He would turn up some time soon.

Had he got stranded in some foreign land? In one of those countries they were going to visit together – Italy perhaps? Or some far eastern place? How often they had imagined southern warmth and sunshine among people who loved to dance and sing – far more cheerful than the romantic music she had learned to play on her piano.

'That strain again, it has a dying fall,' she quoted and shook herself. 'No, I will not feed on sad music but on my happy memories. Come home from those foreign countries, my love, and let us live and laugh together.'

It was late in the day and, sunset coming early on these spring evenings, the sky was turning to pale rose and orange behind the gleam of the sinking sun. She felt his arm round her shoulders, his head leaning on hers and heard his voice softly whispering those loving words: 'Wait for me . . . never forget you . . . Spend our future life together . . .'

She heaved a heavy sigh: 'As long as I have these memories to feed on, I shall wait, my dear.' And the book of plays slid from her knee to the floor.

Dawn Anne Dister

North Lodge Cottage

If I lived in North Lodge Cottage, on the brow of the hill,
I would
       walk every morning beyond Whinney Fell,
frisky dog by my side, all damp with dew. Spend
hours in the garden devouring The Goldfinch

to a back-chirp of birdsong. Have the milkman
bring two pints of gold-top a day, for milk jelly
and cardamon custard. Accomplish a dairy-fed

complexion, paint the woodwork in Mouse's Back,
put a sign on the lintel reading *duck or grouse.*
line the walls with the work of finest of poets. I would

not sit in in silence, yearn to disappear. I would live,
in North Lodge Cottage, and you would be here.

Tammy Swift-Adams

Biographies of Authors and Editor

On retirement, **Gordon Bell** enjoyed using his writing skills for short stories and verse. He has always been obsessed with humour, and volunteering for the MBA Mountain Bothy Association workparties over many years met so many interesting characters from all walks of life – they live with him still, and are in his story.

Stuart Blair is a member of the Dalkeith group. He has had a number of poems published in magazines and anthologies. A first collection awaits any publisher foolish enough to consider one.

Elspeth Brown's writing is now mainly poetry. She has had two books and a pamphlet published and won a joint first prize from Scottish Pen. Recently she has been writing poems and not sending them anywhere but plans to reform in October and get back to work.

Nova Brown is an experienced administrator with extensive knowledge of Government practices. She retired from the Scottish Government in September 2021 after 40 years service in varying posts. She has written a number of published consultation papers and guidance documents. She is currently working on a film script and television series. During her spare time Nova plays bowls and volunteers at Edinburgh Zoo where she passes on her animal knowledge to visitors.

Keith Cornwell's writing has been largely scientific non-fiction but latterly he has transgressed into fiction, albeit with a good dose of facts and fun involved. He studied both engineering and philosophy as an undergraduate student in London. Engineering led to his gainful employment as a researcher, Professor, Dean and such things in Edinburgh and latterly in the Middle East. Philosophy led to him to wondering what it is all about.

Yvonne Dalziel is a Glasgow University M.Litt Creative Writing graduate, lives in Ormiston and is seeking an agent for two unpublished novels.

Dawn Anne Dister was born and grew up in Edinburgh. She moved to Germany after studying modern languages at Edinburgh University. While still at school she also studied Drama at the London Academy of Dramatic Art and went on to direct and act with the Prisma Theatre Group in Speyer which she co-founded in 1968. She stays in North Berwick twice a year and joined Tyne and Esk writers 5 years ago. Since then, she has regularly attended meetings and contributed ideas and texts to North Berwick Writers Group. She writes poetry and short stories in both English and German and is also a member of writing groups in Speyer.

Lorna Dixon has mainly written plays for performance but since joining Tyne and Esk Writers in 2007 has also been trying to hone her skill in writing short stories.

Penelope Durkan does not feel like a writer but can't always believe what slides out between a cheap ballpoint pen and the back of a cereal box. Joining Dunbar Writers earlier this year took more courage than she likes to admit but has turned out to be so much more than expected.

Hannah Faoiléan lives in Roslin, Edinburgh, and loves walking in wild places with her collie. Whenever she's not walking, or working as a pet behaviourist, you will find her reading or dreaming or writing. Hannah has had a poem and short story published in Dream Catcher literary magazine (Stairwell Books), a YA fantasy novel shortlisted for the Chimera Fantasy Awards, a flash fiction runner up piece published in Writing Magazine plus two poems shortlisted in Writing Magazine competitions. Hannah's 'It's a Goat's Life' is based on a real experience.

Moira Galbraith's work experience over the years has included various roles in bookkeeping, catering and in public houses that were nice... and some not so nice... This has given her a wonderful insight into life, people and situations. She enjoys writing and tries to capture life from different angles. Her portfolio includes scripts for television, radio and theatre which have received positive feedback, however her successfully published works include historical and fictional articles and poems and she has been recognised as a visual writer.

Kenny Gilchrist has been a member of the Dalkeith writing group for 20 years. He has had poems published in other Tyne and Esk anthologies and Scrivens, and enjoys reading books on various topics.Kenny has had a short story 'The road to Tynecastle Park' published in *A Sense of Place*.

Billy Graham joined Tyne and Esk Writers in 2004, and with the help of various Creative Writing Fellows has published 19 novellas of different genres. Regardless of genre most include humour.

Arthur Greenan was born in Tranent, in 1940, and reared among Clydesdale he has revived his boyhood love with this recollection of his happiest days as a teenager. The farmer at the Myles, Mr Robert Dykes and Tom Macmillan at East Windygoul let him run freely around their farms. From their horsemen he learned the secrets of the countryside and its residents.

Graham Leake joined the Dalkeith Group of Tyne and Esk Writers in 2002, after his retirement, which followed a career mostly within the sphere of Design – as a practitioner and as a lecturer in Design History. He writes mainly prose with, he hopes, an element of humour.

Jeff Kemp is a writer based in Musselburgh who likes to play with words and has recently needed stronger glasses. Too much information even for the briefest bio-pic.

Emma Lamont studied creative writing at the University of Leeds. She now writes for fun, enjoying themes of local lore and dark fiction.

Jackie Ley is a former college lecturer and graduate of the University of St Andrews where she obtained an M.Litt. in Creative Writing. She has three novels published on Amazon and has recently completed a fourth, set in Northern France, where she lived for several years before returning to Scotland to set up home in North Berwick.

Alison Low's life is lived somewhere between the real world where she writes memoir, and cyberspace writing supernatural and slipstream fiction. In 2022 she organised public readings by local writers as part of the Tide & Time Festival in Dunbar harbour. When she is not writing she is busy running her computer training and IT business. She lives in Dunbar with her husband Bob, and their elderly delinquent tomcat, Tarragon The Terrible.

Ali MacDougall lives in East Linton and has been keeping journals all her life. She joined Dunbar Writers in 2019 and finds that being part of a group that is keen to hear her work and offer valuable feedback has given her courage and confidence. She is now working on a memoir.

Olivia McMahon/Farrington was born in England of Irish parents but has spent the last 50 years of her life in Scotland – mainly in Aberdeen but for the last 4 years in Dunbar. She has published 2 books of poetry and 3 novels. She won the WTYC 2022 for poetry.

For 37 years **Shona Montgomery** worked with The Scottish Government (formerly The Scottish Office, then The Scottish Executive) in several policy areas, writing briefings for Scottish Ministers. In (semi) retirement she thoroughly enjoys exploring creative writing with fellow members of North Berwick Group of Tyne & Esk Writers.

Philippa Ramsden has combined a career in international development with a compulsion to write. She is fascinated by everyday moments, capturing these in poetry, non-fiction and occasional short stories and is working on a memoir. She has contributed short fiction, memoir and poetry to a number of anthologies and journals published in Hong Kong, Myanmar, Mongolia and the UK as well as online publications (including Scrivens) and guest blog articles. Her own blog shares reflections and her story, and she can be found on Twitter and Instagram. Following nearly two decades living and working in Asia and Africa, she returned to Scotland in 2017 somewhat adrift. She has settled in East Lothian, gently unfurling.

Since his arrival in East Lothian last year, **Tony Ruffell** has put his first and only great novel – about the distant past, the near future, society and dislocation – on hold. Meanwhile he tries to develop his writing abilities through short stories, flash fiction and the occasional poem. His themes are sometimes cosmological, often fantastical and seldom serious. Most importantly, he is glad to be learning from his fellow writers how he can create characters, manage dialogue and avoid adverbs. Some good may yet come of it all.

Jock Stein, currently convener of Tyne and Esk Writers, is a minister and musician living in Haddington whose latest book, *Temple and Tartan: Psalms, Poetry and Scotland* can be obtained through www.handselpress. co.uk. He brings experience of the Sheffield steel industry, life in Kenya and Hungary, and managing a 90 bed conference centre to his poetry, which is written in many styles. There is always more to life and poetry!

Cynthia Stephens is a poet and Hispanist, living in Dunbar. She is author of *The Borges Enigma*, Tamesis Books. Her poetry book *Seagulls & Sonnets* features many places she has loved since childhood on a Scottish farm. She used to keep her own chickens, and when at primary school in Belhaven she took presents of eggs to her teachers. She describes this happy school 'Miss Duncan's Academy' in *Growing up in East Lothian 1945-2000*: https://el4.org.uk/growing-up/cynthia-stephens/

Diana Stevens has been a member of Tyne and Esk Writers Dunbar Group since 2011. Two creative writing courses (Open University) encouraged her to try poetry and short stories. A sonnet was commended in the 2017 Vernal Equinox competition. Several Fibonacci poems have been published in the fib review.

Tammy Swift-Adams is a poet and town planner who lives in Dunbar. She joined Dunbar Writers in 2017 and loves its sense of community. She has been writing for about 10 years and from time to time has had poems published, for example in the Interpreter's House, and been a finalist or short/long-listed in competitions, for example Poetry on a Beermat and the Wigtown Poetry Prize.

Brenda Thomson is the daughter of a lighthouse keeper, so lighthouses often feature in her writing. Because her parents were Aberdonians, she sometimes writes poetry and short stories in Doric rather than in English. She has been lucky enough to travel to far-flung places and this, too, is often used as the focus for what she writes.

For many years genealogy was a hobby which culminated in **Malcolm Young** self-publishing his own and his wife's family histories. That done, with the help of the Haddington Writers Group, he has started writing short stories to create answers to puzzles in those histories and to provide a sense of what life might have been like for some of their ancestors. His stories are fictional but based around real people.

* * *

Margaret Skea is a Hawthornden Fellow and multi-award-winning novelist of five historical novels, a short story collection and a contemporary biography, each set in different centuries and continents. Credits include Beryl Bainbridge Award, Neil Gunn Prize, Fish, Mslexia, Rubery, the Historical Novel Society and the BookBrunch Selfies Prize. She has experience of both traditional and self-publishing.

Growing up during 'The Troubles' in Northern Ireland much of her writing is concerned with living within conflict, and the pressures that places on families, relationships and on personal integrity.

Her primary focus in all of her writing is to provide an authentic 'you are there' experience for the reader.

She can be contacted via her website – https://www.margaretskea.com